GROWING
UP NAKED

GROWING

MY YEARS IN BUMP AND GRIND

UP NAKED

LINDALEE TRACEY

DOUGLAS & McINTYRE
VANCOUVER / TORONTO

Douglas & McIntyre Ltd.
1615 Venables Street
Vancouver, British Columbia
V5L 2H1

Canadian Cataloguing in Publication Data
Tracey, Lindalee, 1957–
Growing up naked

ISBN 1-55054-471-3

1. Tracey, Lindalee, 1957– 2.Stripteasers—Biography. I. Title.
PN1949.S7T72 1997   792.7'028'092   C97-910389-4

Editing by Lynn Cunningham
Jacket photograph by Danny Singer
Design and typesetting by Tania Craan
Printed and bound in Canada by Friesens
Printed on acid-free paper

The publisher gratefully acknowledges the support of the Canada Council for the Arts and of the British Columbia Ministry of Tourism, Small Business and Culture.

Excerpts from "Daddy" by Sylvia Plath are reprinted by permission of Faber & Faber Ltd.

For Peter,
because only love matters

Acknowledgments

This journey is a true one, as best I can remember through my notes, journals, letters and news clippings. Names, places and characters have been altered to protect those who wish to keep their secrets. I know what it is to want invisibility.

There are co-conspirators in this book, with whom I share all that is true and beautiful here and whom I absolve of any fault for its flaws. These memories have been lovingly coaxed from me, and sometimes yanked, by the remarkable talent of my editor and dearest friend, Lynn Cunningham, who demanded the truth, however much I winced. Without her I would remain silent and clumsy. And there is Scott McIntyre, who never faltered in his belief or encouragement. His wife, Corky, feeds that strength. Thank you both.

My gratitude goes to the Canada Council, for its unwavering dedication to Canadian authors in these lean and corporate times. And to the Maclean Hunter Arts Journalism program at the Banff Centre for the Arts, and Don Obe, who could see what was coming and embraced it.

And finally, to the strippers I have met and who taught me along the way, I hope I honour you with this.

CHAPTER 1

The Christening

All day I twitch at the beginning and end of myself, watching my face for changes. Practising my walk and turns, talking to myself in other people's voices. I glue sequins to the long black skirt I bought at Zellers, twirling in it and imagining stardom. All day I pick at the skin around my thumbnails, watching *Beverly Hillbillies* reruns. Waiting for the right light, the last cigarette, the guts to leave here.

No one who knows me would believe it. They say I'm tougher than the project girls in Britannia, scared of nothing, crazy. They call me Tric-Trac after the toy cars that race off the track and smash into furniture. Like I'm some kind of retard. I'm not. I have big feelings I hide in my poetry, soft ones that come out hard so they don't get beat. Same thing with being female: I don't like being small or quiet. But my friends don't know how scared I can be or what hurts inside. And I don't show them.

I want to be a stripper but all I know is from the late-night movie I saw once with Natalie Wood playing Gypsy Rose Lee. I remember a lady slipping off long evening gloves, men packed around her like wet fish. I can't tell if the idea is beauty or talent or just being bare naked. But I want it a lot. I think it will make me older, surer and get me the hell out of this girlie-girl world.

I push off toward Eden on a gust of adrenaline, bringing the newspaper ad in case they change their minds: "Eden, the garden of earthly delights. Canada's no.1 strip club now auditioning nude dancers. Great pay, no experience necessary. Bring own music. Must be eighteen."

I find Eden in a rusty part of town, all wheezy with drunks and geezers. It's a tiny door wedged between Hank's Hardware and Gifts and a country music bar. There's a poster in the second-floor window: a jungle with scantily clad women peering through, like a shampoo ad. I climb the stairs all the way into the dark, pushing past the wrought-iron gate

and ticket booth. The carpets and drapes absorb my
sounds as if I'm not here. I smell smoke and cologne,
a downtown smell. Every part of me is on end, reaching into it. At the top the darkness lifts slowly. The
theatre is old, deep; rows of empty seats slope down
to the runway, plush plum velvets and brassy glows,
like Paris or New York. I can't believe I'm in my own
city. The thrill moves up my spine and makes me feel
sneaky.

I hear whispers from somewhere higher and pull
my eyes up. People are bunched on the balcony: two,
three, four women—one naked, white-ass like the
moon. Strippers, I guess. I tiptoe up the stairs toward
them, sucking in air to puff myself up. Willing myself
to look older. Smarter. Funnier. I feel like Annette
Funicello with a pair of Mickey Mouse ears clamped
to my head. "You the auditionee?" one of them asks in
a haughty tone. It's the pink-eyed one with the
Kleenex. "That's all you brought?" The woman stares
disdainfully at my plastic grocery bag. "Good fuckin'
luck," she sneers.

"Away *donc,* Emma." The older woman in a black
negligee yanks her by the hair. Pink-eyes slaps her
hand away: "Fuck off, Yvette." Yvette is more creased
than the others, softer in a way, safer. I move toward
her. "Me, I'm Yvette," she says. "Dat's Emma, dat one's
Ruby." Ruby is the stark naked one, almond-eyed,
curled around a joint. She touches my arm, asks if I
want a toke.

I see a woman kneeling on the floor. "Dat's Sugar,"
Yvette tells me. "Sugar Kane," the blonde adds, not

looking up, not having to. She's perfect, almost porcelain, kneeling over a large glass box. I bend down toward her, then stop abruptly. *Geez!* Inside the glass cage is a leathery coil of muscle, brown and moss green, thick as my leg. She says it's a boa constrictor, part of her act. "I'm the headliner," she says. She looks up, blinking her eyes on like headlights. I stare back, falling into a milky fear. She doesn't want me in there and pushes me out.

The women are silent, as if they're waiting for something to happen. Sugar's hands are cupped prayerlike and I imagine a sacred ritual, incantations, sacrifice. Something dark and bloody. It's stupid. I'm always inventing stupid shit, always placing myself in the middle of a novel, wanting my life to begin. But something does move in Sugar's hands, something alive. She grabs it by the tail and dangles it over the snake. Emma growls that she's fuckin' cruel and to just put the damned thing in. Sugar says Emma's an ignoramus—boa constrictors are almost blind, she has to show him where his food is. Emma wants her to hurry the fuck up because it's getting to her allergies. The mouse claws the air frantically, bending its head back, away from the snake.

I jump as the speakers suddenly crackle like gunfire, some old gal singing "Hey, Big Spender." "Shooow time," Emma groans through her ball of Kleenex. The girls all move in a pack up the stairs. I stay behind with Sugar, trying to make myself small.

Sugar drops the mouse on the boa's head and watches it zigzag across the cage, scurrying away to the farthest corner, trying to climb out. The snake lifts its head, hardening like a bicep, spooking the mouse. The poor thing darts across the cage, back and forth, uselessly. The boa's playing with it, lumbering a little one way, then another, as heavy as death. Sugar smiles. I've only seen brutality close up once, when a neighbour boy stuffed a live bird up a drain pipe. I remember its squawking and the vibration of tiny wings trying to beat free. The boy was pudgy, hard-mouthed. Not lean and doll-faced like Sugar. I want to save the mouse, to snatch it in my hand and run. I want to see it die, too, to know this meanness inside Sugar.

The boa lunges silently, gulping the thing whole. Inch by inch the mouse disappears into the maw, the long pink tail trembling as its front half is consumed. "Their jaws actually dislocate," Sugar whispers. "They can swallow almost anything." I don't think she's talking to me.

"Ladies and genitals...." The speakers boom with a man's deep voice. "Welcome to Eden, the garden of earthly delights. Canada's number-one strip club. In just a few minutes we'll be starting the show with this week's tantalizing lineup of talent. It's guaranteed to tickle your pickle, heat your meat and pop your cork."

Eden is waking around me: spotlights winking and the smell of hot dogs floating into the balconies. A few weak shadows move into their seats, and I feel soft toward them, familiar. They're like all the old men who ran all the old candy stores in my childhood, the Macs and Jacks and Bills. I want to be kind to them, pat them, take away that thing they carry so heavily.

An older man moves toward me, thin and round-shouldered. "You the new girl?" "Yeah," I mutter. He says he's Abe Soloman. Geez, it's the guy I talked to on the phone last week, the owner or co-owner or something like that. He looks tired, sunken in himself, not menacing. But I pull myself up, acutely older.

What if he wants to take off my clothes or hit me up with heroin? What if he wants a blow job? Guys don't like being told no; I learned that hitchhiking. It makes them rear up and swipe at you. Or they get babyish and whiny: "Why not, whynot, whynot?" You have to act stupid when you say no. You have to leave them feeling in charge, as though the no just slipped out of you accidentally, like you're sorry it happened, but there it is, in the air between you. No.

What if this Abe guy says I'm too flat or babyish? "Sure you're eighteen?" he asks mechanically. "Don't I look it?" I lie. Abe shrugs. "Who knows these days? Look at her," and he points at Sugar. "Forty-two but could you guess?" Abe turns away chuckling.

"Damn Jew," Sugar hisses. I stare blankly and she pulls away quickly. I'm glad to be alone where the dark can hide me, where I can run my mind against myself, feeling my own familiarness. I wonder if these are my last minutes as me, if I'll become someone else tonight. I hope so. I don't want to live in pieces anymore: the renegade schoolgirl, the rebellious daughter, the slut, the poetess. Always in danger of being caught, as though I'm guilty of something. I want to grow differently, excessively, noisily. To cross all the borders, to run. Fast. Away.

The men are moving into their seats. Phantoms, I think, the dead. I feel a cold flutter of dread. It's thrilling.

Outside the dressing room I listen to the murmur of women. It holds me like a lullaby, like safer nights when I was a girl and my aunts would fill up on gin. I remember their French, the low, slippery words as they peeled off the skins of their secrets. A wet kind of talk about marriages and men. Then falling asleep with their sound in my ears.

I push the door open and my eyes tingle. The room is like a jewelry box, glittering with shoes, clothes, fluttering feathers. Rhinestones blink and old rads clank. It's a deep, skinny place with a mirror along its side, stinking of sweat and hair spray. Female.

The women concentrate on their transformations and do not see me. Yvette is in the corner with cotton balls between her toes, colouring her nails. Next to her Emma is sneezing and caking white powder on her face. Ruby sits naked on a chair, rolling cigarettes. And at the end, delicate as a princess, is Sugar in frilly white lingerie, pouring from a bottle of ginger ale. I'm surprised, relieved, that they're regular-looking women, pale and imperfect as bank tellers. Just blabbing like girls and barely remarkable, except for the way they live in front of each other, in progress, unfinished.

Ruby hollers at me to take a seat, hooking her foot on the back of a chair and pulling it out. I sit beside her staring at all the hair brushes and perfume bottles. The women's stuff is spread out like separate armies: lipstick, lotion, curling irons, pictures of pets and men. I plunk down my own meagre kit: Maybelline eyeliner, liquid rouge, a cheap blue comb. I hide my costume under the counter.

"Yo, Yvette," a man's voice drawls from the far end of the room. "Fahve minutes."

Ruby sinks into the chair, spreading her legs and studying herself with a hand mirror. I can't help looking. She asks if I think cunts are beautiful. I guess so. "They're like flowers," she tells me. "They've got these petals. See?"

Ruby tilts her pelvis slightly so I can peek in. She says labia majora is the fat one and labia minora, the teeny, tiny one inside. I can smell the muskiness of Ruby's body, the dampness between her legs—it's exhilarating, I've never been allowed so close to another girl before. Ruby tells me she thinks she's got the most beautiful cunt in the world. It's not conceit, she says, it's just the way she was born. But Sugar thinks Ruby's gross, snapping the words out from across the room. Ruby argues that there's nothing gross about bodies. "It's cheap," Sugar's says firmly. Emma asks what Sugar thinks the guys want out there.

"Dey want a show," Yvette cuts in. "Now somebody 'elp me wit dis." Emma pulls the zipper up on Yvette's satin gown. But Sugar can't stop her taunting:

if Ruby can't dance, she can always spread her pussy. Emma laughs viciously.

"Isn't that just a little hypocritical coming from a chick who..."

"I can dance!" Ruby shouts.

"...rubs men's ties between her legs?"

Sugar's face tightens as if she's been caught at something. Emma can't compare her to Ruby, she snarls. What she does is illusion, pretend for the Old Man. Emma tells her to fuck off.

"Sugar! Emma!" Yvette thunders. The women stiffen. *"C'est assez.* Enough. You have to show your pussy, Ruby, dat's your business. Me, I don't want to see. So more private. *Oui?"* I can feel currents under the surface, something complicated. Yvette doesn't like Ruby but her feelings are mixed with disgust. Maybe even fear. Yvette's the queen around here.

The room settles into a trembling hush. Sugar grins like a cat. A stubby, misshapen man comes through the door and I think he might be a customer. "Hey, Worm, got my Craven A?" Emma hollers. *Worm?* He smiles and says it's short for Werner. "Worm's okay," Ruby reassures me. He's our favourite gofer, right? If I need anything, smokes, tampons, Southern Comfort, Worm'll get it. "But you have to give me the money first," Worm says brightly.

Worm's not old like I first think. He's more like a big kid, maybe twenty, goofy and a little retarded under dark square hair. He moves through the room making deliveries and the women give him tips.

Sugar's the most generous, offering a five-dollar bill. Worm stops at Yvette, staring at the cotton balls between her toes. "Can I pull 'em out, Miss Yvette?" he pleads.

"Yes, Werner, you can. Den off you go." After Worm leaves Yvette yanks up her net stockings and tears a hole in them with her pointy red nails. "It's for effect," she explains. "A little beet of imperfection relax de crowd. Dat's it and dat's all."

"Ladies and gentlemen, direct from Montreal, would you please welcome the naughty and sensuous Mademoiselle Yvette."

"Direct from fucking Mechanicsville," Emma chortles.

I scramble to the door, craning to see the stage. Yvette twinkles in a single beam of light, floating through the pitch blackness. The crowd whistles and hoots, especially the old guys, as she sashays down the runway, shimmering in her gown, glamorous as a film star—this is what I remember from the late-night movie. Her face and hands are so white against the black, so small and delicate. The song is one of those corny Dean Martin ones.

Yvette is regal in an old-fashioned way, but she isn't beautiful and that surprises me. I thought stripping was about looks. She doesn't really dance, either, just walks and twirls and stops a lot. Her show reminds me of strip poker: she takes something off in every song. When she's ready to do it, she leans down from the runway and pretends to need help. The guys seem grateful, reaching up to unlock her dress, her corset, pulling clumsily at her stockings. Loving the chance to be useful, to be envied by each other.

Yvette keeps the last bits to herself, mysteriously unclipping her panties from her hips. Underneath is a gold triangle against her crotch, invisibly fastened. I like the hardware, the clips and clamps. They are as reassuring as kitchen gadgets in housewares—the remarkable K-Tel Dicer, the egg slicer, the garlic press—culminations of precise logic. Safe.

Yvette sneaks into her nakedness, a blur of white skin against a dark background, vague and indistinguishable from any other woman. But as I watch the men watching Yvette, her body, bony and pear-shaped, begins to separate from her personality.

The younger men wear belligerent faces, bored of Yvette, or frightened. They talk loudly, snigger. It makes me angry. But the older men enjoy Yvette and are eager for her eyes to meet theirs. They applaud heartily at the end, and she twirls a negligee around herself and bows dramatically. When she leaves the stage she creeps through the dark at the back of the crowd, climbing the stairs half naked. It makes her look diminished.

Emma asks me if I've ever danced before. I have, I lie. It isn't exactly a lie. I've danced with the buskers on the Sparks Street Mall. When they've let me. "How 'bout you?" Ballet and all the middle-class stuff. Still has her pointes, she says. I nod, pretending to understand. "See?" Emma lifts a thin, slippered foot right over her head. "It's lost on these johns, but fuck, grab their money and run." Emma laughs and makes pig noises. I laugh too so she won't know I am afraid of her hardness. Emma's taking poli-sci at Carleton. Political science. She's not growing old in this place, she spits. "Here, you might need this." She rolls a tube of lipstick to my part of the counter. My heart unfreezes.

"Fahve minutes, Emma." The voice drawls from the sound booth again. Emma hurries into her costume. She grabs Ruby's joint and sucks in deeply. "Shit!" The dressing room door opens and Emma hurries to pinch off the lit end. "Somebody been smoking? Ruby?" "It's Fat-Ass Glad Ass, the owner's girlfriend," Emma whispers. "A real snake."

"Hi, Gladys," Sugar chirps. The short, dark, manicured girl unclenches her face for a moment. "Oh hiiii," she says all honeyed. "Be terrific if you did your snakes tonight. Johnny's got the Rough Riders coming down." Gladys looks at me as if she smells something bad. "So you're the new one," she says. I hide my thoughts behind dog eyes. "It's not who ya know, it's who ya blow," Emma whispers. Gladys hunches. "Excuse me? I heard that. Tell Ruby I'm docking her five bucks for smoking." "Hey, that's not fair...." Gladys smiles viciously and says life's not fair. Then she slams the door behind her.

Emma grimaces—"Spoilt little shit." Sugar says Emma should learn to shut up. "Or suck ass," Emma snaps back. Maybe Sugar could teach her how to do that. "Hiiii, Gladys," she mimics. Sugar says she doesn't think people should do drugs in here. Emma reminds her that alcohol is a drug. "Oh, I'm a drunk?" "Does the Pope hate women?" Then Emma darts out the door.

"Ladies and gentlemen, Eden proudly presents the tiny and talented..."

"Eat shit," Emma's voice wafts up through the club.

"He's talking about her tits," Ruby says. "She doesn't have any," Sugar adds.

"...Emma Goldman."

Emma leaps onto the stage with a blast of "In-a-Gadda-Da-Vida." She's like something from a horror movie: screaming, combustible. "HELLO, YOU Y CHROMOSOMES." The older men pull back. The scruffier ones applaud and holler from the back. Emma's wearing black tights and tutu and she's got a set of antlers on her head. She prances on tiptoe, smiling down haughtily at the frightened faces. She's long and thin and bendable like a ballerina.

Emma's nakedness comes slowly, clumsily, like slapstick. She isn't trying to be sexy. She blows her nose right there on stage, then marches up and down, yelling at the men: "Hey, you in the wanker row. Can I see both your hands!" I don't know if she's really angry. The men in ties and the older ones twitch, looking hopefully to the stairs for the next dancer, trying to keep their eyes off her. Emma forces their attention.

"You looking for your wife? She's on next." The front guys cringe while the back ones hoot. Somehow Emma reverses reality so that she's watching the men and they're watching each other. She's the cat and they're the mice. "I'm sorry. Am I too aggressive?" Emma kneels on the stage all soft, stroking the straight man's face. "MY PAROLE OFFICER THINKS SO TOO."

Emma gives no safety, no comfort. Just hard bare knuckles coming at them with her thundering rock'n' roll. She's scary to watch. And magnificent. She stands on her hands for almost an entire song, undressing upside down. It's Olympian the way she pulls her panties off with her toes, inch by inch. Even the businessmen are impressed. Then Emma springs to her feet, not bowing but bending her bare ass to the crowd and making farting sounds. I realize she's an artist. The first one I know. Squirrelly like one. Layered.

Emma widens me in myself, pushing me to thoughts I've never had, through rules I thought were written in stone. I think this makes a difference on my face. But the mirror gives me my same old plain one, not even pretty. Yvette suggests false eyelashes. I apply the glue and manoeuvre one to my eyelid. It sticks on at an angle like an eyebrow. Yvette howls. I try many more times until the lashes are fastened. They flap against my eyes like wings. The women stare approvingly. Emma says it looks good. I'm a *vedette,* Yvette chirps. I'm confident enough to pull out my costume.

It's a meagre heap of fabric I grab from the shopping bag: long sequined skirt and jacket, floppy red hat I found in the park. Frilly underwear from Sears and a raccoon stole that makes Emma sneeze. I look like Janis Joplin on her album cover. Something left in an attic. Emma thinks for the right word, squinting through red rabbit eyes. Yvette says it's antique. Emma agrees quickly: "Baroque." Whatever that means. Sugar tugs off my moulting raccoon tail and wraps me in her red feather boa. I'm surprised by her kindness. "Something borrowed, something new," she singsongs childishly. Sugar tries fastening her eyes on me but they keep sliding off.

The sound man emerges from his booth and takes the joint Emma offers. He's tall and gangly, with a ponytail and kind eyes, I think. Emma says he's American, a draft dodger from South Carolina. Ric asks if I've brought any music. I follow him into the small dark hole with my stack of albums. It's like an airplane cockpit in here, blinking with gadgets. I give Ric a piece of paper with my scribbled instructions.

"See them big lights there?" he points to the stage. "Them things'll blind ya, so don't look straight at 'em, okay? And don't get too close to them footlights. Those suckers'll fry ya. Got that?"

Uh huh. He says he knows I'll do fine. For an instant I believe him. But my certainty fades when I see Sugar on stage. She's so smooth and pink, girlish, I'm raggedy and big-boned, not cherry pie like her. I like running, climbing, pushing into the world, into men I like, hard, hurried. Exhausting myself. Not worrying about fluffy sweaters or keeping parts of me folded and neat. Natural comes closest to what I am, I guess. But these guys want something more wounded and thin or round and big-chested, not something in between like me.

I'm in a flurry trying to line up what I've learned, trying to remember the order of things coming off: dress, feathers, panties? No. Feathers, dress, bra, panties. "What about shoes?" Yvette asks. I haven't brought any. Don't want any. *"Non, non, non.* You don't make a show wit no shoes. Dat's it and dat's all." She plunges into her costume bag, pulling out a pair of black high heels. Very high. I wobble like a stilt walker. Yvette says I can buy good ones later from Vachek the shoeman when he comes in next week. Emma asks if I've got a wrap, something to come back from the stage in. I haven't thought of that either, haven't even imagined beyond the beginning of this night. Emma gives me a long blue silk one.

"One mooore minute," Ric hollers.

I'm suddenly cold, shivering. I wish I could stop it. I wouldn't mind being drunk. Emma whispers, "Good luck, kiddo." The kiddo part annoys me. Yvette warns me to keep the shoes on till the end. I barely hear her as I tumble into a big black pit.

I creep unsteadily down the stairs, keeping to the shadows; feeling my cold, wet smallness against the dark mass of men. I'm afraid, not of them, but of myself, of my own tight untalentedness. I feel legless backstage, as if I'm floating behind the velvet curtain, waiting to be announced. I try concentrating so I won't miss the cue. On the dirty back wall strippers have left their epitaphs:

"Donna Duz but for a price."

"Emma is a boy."

"I smell Ruby."

"Sugar is leaving her brain to medical science (if they can find it)."

"Ladies and gentlemen, on the occasion of her very first performance, a warm welcome, please, for our auditioning dancer...."

I have no name, I realize in the last hurried moment of myself. Somewhere there is a chorus of cheering strippers but I can't see them. I can't see anything. I heave toward the light, toward the familiar screeching of Janis Joplin's "Take a Piece of My Heart." The footlights are blinding. I'm all antennae, feeling for the edge of the stage, scared of falling into the big blackness of eyes. I stay in the middle, twisting my arms and legs, tangling up in myself.

Faces begin to emerge from the blur, staring up at me, but I can't tell if they are scowling or smiling. I try to breathe, to slow down, but I throw off the feathers too soon, and then there's nothing left to hold onto. I reach into the air, inventing shapes and snaky movements, trying to get control of my spiraling body. My stomach lurches, I have to stop spinning. I nearly fall over. It's the shoes, I have to get out of the shoes. Yvette flashes into my mind and I chance the walk to the edge of the runway, penguinlike. Rows of faces tilt up and I stick my foot out at them. An old man in a porkpie hat reaches up and pulls the shoes off.

The old man's smile steadies me. I leap up on my bare feet, jumping through the air. I'm beginning to find my confidence, my rhythms, following the music, unwinding myself.

I throw down my hat and try pulling off my skirt but it won't come off easily. I yank it up over my head, fumbling blindly beneath it. Suddenly I'm impatient with clothes, with poses, with fear itself. There is no more fear, no self, just a fast, gushing emptying, a discarding. I rip off my bracelets, beads, even the eyelashes. If I could, I would pull out my hair and throw it at the men.

But the bra won't come off. The frilly black, back-fastened twenty-eight dollar bra from Sears won't unclip. I back into the curtain, wiggling and jiggling, dressing up my terror with convulsive motions. Time stops as my mind fastens onto that single clip. My arms splay as I claw at the hook in the back. Finally the damned thing springs open like a clam.

I tear across the stage, sinews stretching, cartwheeling the length of the runway. I'm in my body, at the fearsome shadows of first perceptions. I'm swelling in myself, multiplying, becoming invincible, fearless. I'm hot and cold with sweat on my eyes and belly, showering the men with my body's rain. I'm even slowing down a little, daring to peek into the hard husks of faces that stare from the dark, seeing a smile, an outstretched hand, a widened eye. I'm feeling the heat of a hundred men, their attention on me.

Then the music ends and the lights go down. I hold myself still, reaching into the dark, into the mood, holding my pose like a statue. The entire theatre stares vacantly back at me. I don't know what to do. I cover myself and back away, feeling for the seam in the curtain, plunging finally behind it. The wall is cold and I'm flattening against it, feeling a thud in my eardrums.

Eden is spitting me out, dismissing me.

"Ladies and gentlemen, a big round of applause for...." Don't bother, don't bother, I wince, as the wave of noise penetrates the curtain. I don't want pity. But the applause is loud, genuine. When Worm fishes me out from behind the curtain, I understand why the men took so long to applaud. They didn't know the show was over. I'd forgotten to take off my panties. I stumble up to the balcony, through the men's stares, feeling gigantic. The girls press in, making a warm, sticky circle around me. Yvette keeps railing about taking off my shoes. The girls imitate my dancing, laughing at me.

"Yooou need a, a...name," Sugar mumbles. Ruby grins. "Yeah! Somethin' with the word Pussy in it." Sugar doesn't take the bait. *"Non!"* Yvette cuts in. "Someting young and a little beet fresh." "How 'bout Ila Dicks?" Emma offers. "Get it? She loves dicks." "Or Ila Cox," Ruby says.

"Fond of. Fonda, dat's nice. Fonda someting."

"Fonda Peters," I yell. The women hoot their approval. I beam with the certainty of my own existence. I've been christened.

The Beautiful Janis Joplin Dancer,
We saw your show last night and considered you to be the outstanding performer of those we saw. So you ask why am I writing you this letter.

Like most human beings you must want to know what your audience thinks of you. So here is my opinion. You are gorgeous! Your face, your hair, your smile and your body are all simply gorgeous. You are in the category with the tops in any men's magazine, such as *Playboy.*

Your show should be seen not only by men but also by women because many could learn a great deal from you to make them far greater partners. You look like you could drive a man clean out of his mind!—with pleasure! Wow!

I will consider it a real honour for you to take the time to drop me a note. I am 44 and divorced. 180 pounds, 5'9" with reasonable appearance, although I have been told I was handsome. I earn my living as a salesman.

Why do I want to meet you? I would like to touch you, I liked what I saw and would like to see more of it. I would like to talk with you because I feel your personality and mind matches your body. Eagerly awaiting your reply.
Harold

Maybe there's something that creates the urge to be a stripper, or the confidence, something I share with those girls at Eden. I remember starting normally, growing in the low rumble of my mother's hope and whispers, curving around her like skin. It was warm there, and my body felt good and sturdy until the sickness came, the rheumatic fevers. Maybe that's when the separation began.

They were long years of sickness, of being stuck in hospitals and at home, away from school and other children. I remember my heart's uneven beating, and lying in bed for a year so still no one knew if I was growing. When I got up and walked again it was with dying children in a special school, out of the light of normal lives. My mind grew secretly, dreaming in primary colours of flying or running, of saving orphans. Sometimes I imagined my own dying, savouring the tragedy, surging in grief for myself. I was so alone in there, so out of my body. When I got better I hurried into adolescence. I was clumsy as a geek, and as hopeful.

But the other girls were shrinking, becoming unsure in their changing shapes. I didn't want their falseness, how they hung like ripe grapes, full and limp, around the hard stalks of boys in the schoolyard, intent on being hurt or on hurting each other. I welcomed my own womb's blood, dabbing it on my fingertips to show them: "Look, look." But they retreated from me, pinching their faces like trolls, insisting on invisibility that was more bitter than being alone.

They grew away from me that year, stiffly, perfectly, all in a row like pale blooms in winter. I grew, too, in the warm flush of delinquency and the backseats of cars. I learned about running, hiding, lying. I couldn't follow the usual patterns of growing, escaping instead to the streets, down highways—excessive and hungry—among the dangerous boys. But even they wanted good girls, or frightened ones. Someone tame to dangle from their belt loops. Someone limp. Femaleness was complicated and tight-fitting, like a noose around my neck. I didn't know where to learn about it, except through my own skin.

I wanted to be moral and keep my balance. I wanted to be authentic, too, to try on all my selves. Sex and bad attitude weren't at the core of it like the schools and counsellors said. Freedom was, sanity, self. I would have joined the circus if I could. I wanted somewhere to fit in. Maybe I can now in Eden.

There are things I don't know yet, parts of being a stripper I can't imagine. But I want to be good at something more than just surviving. I want to learn how other girls become female and full, I want to claim my own self fiercely. Honestly.

CHAPTER 2

Backstage at the Girlie Show

I work two weeks for half pay, learning the ways of the place and what I can do here. Learning to answer to my new name. My old buddies still call me Linda, which sounds so private now. They're slack-jawed about my stripping and tell me to watch out I don't get arrested for being underage. I am something bigger than them suddenly, floating away from their lives. My friends are here now, at Eden. So my world grows bigger and smaller at the same time. But Eden is a complicated place, crisscrossed with borders and allegiances. And angry interruptions.

One night I hear a slamming door and sharp voices behind me in the balcony. "Here we go," Emma whispers. A man and woman are arguing over money, shrieking at each other, their lives spilling out like stuffing. The customers notice too and fidget in their seats. The braver ones squint up into the balcony. Ric jacks the music up, drowning out the yelling. The whole club strains harder to listen. Emma tells me it's Johnny, Abe's partner, and that he and Gladys go at it every couple of nights. "It's worse on full moons. Real classy."

It is Abe the peacemaker who comes bounding up the stairs, telling them to pipe down. Gladys yells at him to eat shit. Then she stomps down the stairs, past us strippers. "Scram," Emma tells me. "Get outa here."

The girls start scattering in all directions but it's too late. Johnny Mervin comes out of the office like a bear from its den, scanning the club. He reminds me of Gino Vanelli, coifed hair, Italian suit, a gold spoon hanging down his chest. He barks at Ruby and she slumps on the stairs, caught. Does she mind working the cash till her next show? It's not a question. Ruby sighs and goes down the stairs to the wicket to replace Gladys. The rest of us rush back to the dressing room muttering curses.

I learn to duck in Eden, from Johnny and even from the other girls. They try to claim me for them-selves, telling me secrets about each other because my ears are new. Because I'm still invisible. There are two things they all want me to know: that they're better than this place and that the golden age of stripping has either yet to arrive or has already been. I hope it's still on the way. But Yvette says clubs are different now; men's eyes have detached from their minds. She says they're afraid of her now, of her age. They make fun of her sagging ass and varicose veins, as if those are her only features. Yvette pities their lack of imagination. Sometimes I feel sorry for her.

The girls are smaller, too, she says, without playfulness or intelligence. They aren't as professional now, just acting out the patterns of their wounds, reducing themselves to their physical components, like Ruby. "Dose damn spreads," she says, hacking out her fury. "Dat's de end, eh?"

But that's the part that confuses me. When I finally see Ruby's show, it's not gross like I expect. Ruby sprawls over the sides of a child's wading pool, naked and oblivious. Almost asleep. A single leg creeps into the air, then the other, rubbing together like lovers. It's a slow thing, simple, beads of water trickling down her legs, the perfect bulging of muscle and bone, shiny and wet. My eyes burn from not blinking. Ruby seems so alone, so private, as if she's at home in her own bathtub. She doesn't look at the men or even notice them. She watches only herself. Ruby's legs untangle finally, spreading slowly, widely, fearlessly. It is like watching a painting coming alive, watching life becoming human. My own body tingles: maybe *this* is striptease, this physical freedom and wide-openness.

But I'm afraid, too, and it mixes with my excitement. Afraid of the stern old woman who lives in my brain, of her warnings. *Nice girls, smart girls, good girls don't spread their legs in public.*

As the lights go down I watch men cluster by the curtain, wanting to press money into Ruby's hands, hovering around her worshipfully. Not a single one pushes against her or touches. Only Sugar does, shoving past her en route backstage. Ruby doesn't look at the money—maybe it's not polite. She holds it delicately in her open hands and stares off into the distance, like a Madonna.

It's a weird image and I take it home with me, thinking about the strange decorum of stripping: a girl can spread her legs, but she can't be seen acting greedy. I preserve it in my secret place, a poem, the first one I write here:

> *Lips, breasts, legs spread*
> *Unthreaded spools of womanness*
> *The only thing at the Girlie Show*
> *the clients never see*
> *Are the girlies counting their money.*

The old man Marcel, the collapsible one from Quebec, likes me. Says I'm fresh and funny. He thinks it's nice I don't look down on him. I'm not so good yet, not really a professional, but the old man and his friends forgive me, bringing little cards and presents: stuffed animals and gold things. Even Worm brings me packs of Number 7 cigarettes. Marcel and the others are like a warm blanket around me, snug and close. But sometimes I want to kick them off, I don't want to feel their needs on top of me. I'm not sure who I should be collecting around me, how they define my place here. There are so many classes of strippers, I guess it depends what I call myself.

There are eleven phrases Emma and I have collected to describe what we do: bump and grinder, burlesque dancer, disrober, ecdysiast, exotic dancer, nude dancer, nudie, peeler, stripper, stripteaser, topless dancer. Emma calls herself a stripper because she says it's the most honest word. It's a harder, modern one that keeps off the old guys. But some girls like "exotic dancer." Sugar says it's classier. She fascinates me most. I study her intently, thoroughly. But she's dangerous to watch, asking me if I'm a lezzie when she catches me staring. Ruby warns me that she's messed up—foster homes, shit like that. Wacko.

I keep my vigil, watching from the balcony when Sugar dances. She's luminous on stage, like a sea anemone, absorbing every current, every mood, in a constant act of becoming. Sugar pulls light into herself, becoming perfect from every angle, every viewpoint. She wears her Spanish costume like a souvenir doll: perfect black hat, bolero jacket, flounced skirt and little red shoes that look like hooves. The geezers love her, especially the one in front with the twenty-dollar bills, the Old Man. I keep watching Sugar, looking for clues to becoming myself, my stage self. I want to be great.

Johnny and Gladys want me to be great too. Sort of. They think I should have my own routine and suggest a little girl act. I gag. I want something older and mature, not babyish. I look for a persona, flipping through Hollywood magazines and library books. I don't want to get stuck in a hoop skirt playing Little Bo Peep.

Cavewoman: Raquel Welch—2 Million Years BC//need skins, drums, rock. Expensive. Music? "Ally Oop." "In the Jungle"—Sugar's got it. Kill Sugar.

Countess: Garbo—Camille//Long nightie, candles, satin sheets, definitely need long hair. Music? Classic shit. Die naked, too weird?

Spacegirl: Jane Fonda—Barberella//rocket, suit, gadgets, music?? "2001: A Space Odyssey." "In the Year 2525."

Female Taxi Driver? Music: Harry Chapin's "Taxi," "Drive My Car"—Beatles. Collapsible car frame (oh sure), zipper-sided pants. Expensive but cool.

I stop when I find Marlene Dietrich in a big gold coffee-table book. I am lured by her looks and an obscure old film. *Blue Angel,* 1929. It's a small fact, hard and precise, the prize of my own research, the first one. *Blue Angel,* 1929. I say it like a film expert.

I like how Marlene looks in her top hat and garters. She's many-faced, any-faced, ambiguous and female, cutting a path through my imagination. For days after I scurry through the five and dimes and Salvation Army depots, patching together a Dietrich outfit, negotiating around the good cheer of nosy old matrons—"A school play, dear?"—their eyebrows arching over my weird purchases: cheesy black garter belt, old satin lounge dress, tuxedo and, the rarest of all, a collapsible top hat. These are all parts of my new self, as precious as hope. I buy black Italian pumps from Vachek the shoeman, the philosopher guy with the accent.

I practice in my studio apartment. I don't know how to dance or build a story line into a show. Sugar knows but she ignores me. Ric can see—"Good choice," he says when he eyes the Dietrich album under my arm. "Lady with the million-dollar legs." He lumbers back into his hole beside the dressing room.

Ric is older and American and I imagine that gives him a bigger, more complicated personality. He's genteel, too, in a southern sort of way, never leering, treating us like ladies dressed for the opera. But he's closed off to us strippers—private, forbidden, Sugar's old man. After five weeks, there are only three things I know for certain about him: he loves smoking grass, he thinks Johnny Mervin is an asshole and he hates the U.S. army.

Ric tells me and Emma that before he deserted his Green Berets killed chickens with their ba-yer teeth. "And good God did chicken blood taste like sheeit." I try to penetrate the logic of men chomping on chickens. Were they going to bite their way through Vietnam? But it gives Ric a darker, stickier authority, a knowledge I want to travel into.

Whaddaya mean about the million-dollar legs? I ask him. He says he heard Dietrich got them Lloyds of London insurance people to insure her legs for one million American dollars. He can't work it out in Canadians funds but she was something real big. "You doin' a Dietrich show?" He offers to help.

We begin our rehearsals in the late afternoons, at the end of October. The club is dark and cold. I shiver and talk incessantly. Ric sits up in his booth, aiming his lights on me, pouring heat into a circle on the stage. I go over and over my routine, tipping my top hat, marching in straight lines down the runway. Matching my steps to the music, adding small, precise flourishes and twirls. Undressing smoothly, slowly, in economic motions. Practising gracefulness and the complicated act of unrolling stockings down my leg. They always get hooked on my toes. Ric is vaguely encouraging. When I'm undressed I move and speak in shapes and shadows. In fingertips and hips and thighs. Inside myself, beyond.

Sometimes I ask his opinion and Ric talks back over the microphone. I stand in the darkness feeling his voice vibrating inside me. Sometimes I don't hear the meaning of the words at all, just their sound: the wetness of his tongue, the slow, low death of his breath. Once he tells me I'm a very good dancer. It's the first time anyone has said this to me. Then he turns on the lights and says the rehearsal's over, as if I've done something wrong. It doesn't bother me being naked around Ric or anyone else. But something makes me stiff around him. I hold my stomach in, clench my thighs, wanting to be beautiful in my everyday nakedness.

After a few weeks, Sugar begins appearing, first skulking like a stray dog, then stomping around loudly. When we can't ignore her Ric dims the lights and ends the rehearsal. I try to make friends with Sugar, to pull her in, but she refuses. Sometimes I wait until the last show when she's full of gin to snag her into a conversation, a friendship, a revelation. Sometimes I try at the beginning of the set, like tonight, before we're on each other's bad sides. I think my rehearsals are going well, I tell her. "I bet," is all she says. I feel the room tense. Ruby shakes her head, warning me. I ask Sugar how she leans over her hip in that pose. "Oh, you like that," she asks in a silky way. I tell her I think she's a great dancer. Sugar smiles at herself in the mirror while Emma gestures that she's going to throw up.

Sugar says I might be good too if I wasn't such a spaz. Yeah, I know, I say, laughing eagerly like a retard. Like Worm. Then Sugar's eyes fasten on me suddenly. "What the hell do you want from me?" she asks. I tell her I think we could.... The words fall to the floor between us. "Help each other, be friends?" Sugar sneers. "I don't want to be your goddamned friend. Call yourself a stripper? You don't even have a goddamned show. Just bringing the whole place down...." I am stinging in my smallness. In my rage. I don't understand why Sugar hates me so much, what I've done to her.

Yvette warns Sugar to lay off—"She's practising, *non?*" Sugar turns around angrily: "If that's what she calls it."

"*Arrêt, donc.* Okay?"

Sugar catches my reflection in the mirror, narrows her eyes. "I'm not gonna help you. And my old man's not gonna help you. So back off." I hold my eyes hard against Sugar, pushing deep into her fear as if I know something about her. I don't show my soreness, that I want to bend her head backwards until it snaps. I don't show that to any of them. I look around the dressing room but nobody looks back. Ric shouts angrily that he needs to see Sugar right *now*. She disappears into the sound booth and closes the door.

"Act like an asshole, get treated like an asshole," Emma I-told-you-sos. Her eyes are clear tonight and she rolls them into her head. "Idiot," she says. "You sucked up to her. Never suck up to a drunk." "But she is a good dancer," I insist.

"So what? She knows already."

"Why can't we help each other?" I ask. "What's wrong with that?" A grin spreads over Emma like a sore. What am I, Pollyanna? I tell her I don't know who Pollyanna is. Emma seems exasperated. "This is not Brownies! She's not going to help you. So leave her alone." Ruby passes me a lit joint and nods her head in agreement. I take a deep haul. Sugar's one of Johnny's favourites, Ruby warns me. I shouldn't piss her off.

The sound door opens and Sugar steps out. Her eyes are smudged and wet. I don't let her see me looking. The other girls turn too. A few minutes later Ric calls me into the booth. Sugar's eyes burn into me. Ric apologizes, asks if I can rehearse tomorrow. He talks loudly so everyone can hear. I think it's deliberate. I tell him I don't want to rehearse right now but his tone hardens like an order. "Look, just be there. It'll be cool."

The night passes slowly, dangerously. Sugar drinks hard, growing poisonous. The rest of us hurry out of her way. Emma takes her turn at the snack bar without even complaining, serving hot dogs and big gobs of philosophy. She's on another crusade, tarted up more than on stage: tight bodysuit, red feathers, inviting looks. The guys swarm the counter just like she calculates. Some she has to swat away, most she gets to sign her marijuana petition. Last week it was some California grape boycott.

As intermission ends, Ric cranks up George Carlin's "Seven Words You Can Never Say on Television." Emma and I scream it together: "Shit, piss, fuck, cunt, cocksucker, motherfucker and tits." There. We feel better.

"The minute you walked in the joint, I could tell you were a man of distinction, a real big spender...." Yvette is strutting down the runway in her white satin gown and feathered headdress when I hear the commotion. More like a moan. Gladys and Abe are in the balcony. Johnny and Ric both rush toward them. Gladys keeps repeating the same words, "Are you sure?" Abe nods. "Are you goddamn sure?" Abe nods again. "This is a goddamned mess. This can shut us down." Ric begins poking a stick at the overhead pipes as Johnny shines a flashlight. Sugar is beside her snake cage, rocking on her heels and moaning. The snake is gone. Holy shit!

Gladys snaps at us to get back in the dressing room, that it looks bad for the customers. We refuse. Not with a snake loose in the club. Sugar whimpers and points at me; "It's her," she says. "She did it. She let my snake escape." Me? How can she think that? Or maybe it's retaliation. I can't see into her tangled circuitry.

Everyone stares accusingly at me. Emma says it's bullshit. I was with her the whole intermission. Johnny squints at us as though we're bugs. We stare back, hoping he'll fire Sugar for being such a drunken liar. But no. He says we've got fifty-five minutes to sober her up, and tells Emma to get coffee. Emma barks back, saluting him. "Yes, *mon commandant.*" One day she's going to get it.

We move through Eden cautiously, slowly, going two at a time to the bathroom, checking our costumes. "Look in de arms," Yvette warns. Worm and a couple of gofers keep after the snake, prodding the pipes with broom handles.

Sugar is settling down; at least she's quiet. But the far-off look remains, and the danger. She whispers to me the first moment we're alone, "I know what you're doing." I pretend I don't hear her. "You want to fuck my old man. Just like every chick in this place. Only I won't let you." When Ruby walks in Sugar goes dead quiet, just smirking at me in the mirror. Her next words are almost inaudible: "I'm going to get you." I know she will.

Later, when I do my Janis Joplin show, the other women sit in the balcony to watch, wanting to hold me up, I guess. But I don't see Sugar among them. After my show, worried faces pull me up the stairs. Ruby blurts out that she went nuts, totally nuts. I look at Yvette. "She was so drunk. She...."

Inside the dressing room everything goes watery, wiggly, as if I'm looking through a giant pool. My Marlene Dietrich costume is in shreds. The tuxedo's arms have been hacked off and part of the tail. The top hat is crushed, stomped on. Everyone's staring at me, looking sorry. I try hard not to cry but my shoulders heave and tears leak out.

"It's okay, we'll fix it," Ruby coos like an older sister. Emma promises the bitch'll pay for it. "Come on, get up." Ric is behind me, pulling me up. He says he'll take me home. I let Ric lift me up, I let them all hold me and dress me and put on my coat like I'm made of straw. But it's Ric's hands I feel most, the touch of his fingers on my arms, face, hands. "I'm so sorry," he whispers gently.

Yvette kisses me good night and tells me to take him. "Dat's it. Dat's all." I nod.

The night is cold when we leave the club. Ric holds my arm to steady me. As we walk across the street a small plaintive voice swells. "I'm sorry. I'm really, really sorry. Please, Ric."

Sugar stands on the sidewalk, washed out and vacant looking. Like a whore. "Please, Ric. I can change. I really can." Neither of us looks back.

CHAPTER 3

The Old Broads

I sit in the cab on the way to Yvette's house, imagining her on her heap of pillows, curled into the sheets, following the threads of her dreams back to the dance hall and her own young self. Back to the boys. I like to put my mind there, in Yvette's favourite place. She's told me how soft the men were then, with their open faces pressed against hers on those last nights before death. Jean-Luc, François, Etienne. No, Yvette's mind always detours around the thought of him. She never talks about her husband.

She says her *maman* didn't approve of the war effort, warned her not to go to the Montcalm— *"Ce n'est pas notre guerre"*—it's not our war. *"Sont des maudit loups, là*—they're damned wolves there. But her mother was wrong, Yvette says. It was everyone's war. The soldiers weren't wolves, they were children dressed in rough wool uniforms, scared of dying, of living, scared as hell in their Catholic souls of the needs they pressed against her. Yvette had sneaked into the hall and danced with the boys, holding them close and sometimes kissing them. Sometimes more. They smelled the same in their musky wet wool and lime-scented aftershave. Maybe she wondered how many would come back alive. Maybe it was too dark a pit.

She received their last gifts graciously: dinners and petrol and once even a live chicken! *Maman* took it from her silently, accusingly, imagining the sin behind it. But she was wrong. The boys came to Yvette afraid of their own cruelty, of what they'd learned at camp. They wanted to leave something decent of themselves behind, something noble, even the rough ones. Yvette accepted their fumblings, their need to be remembered. It stopped the grief from swallowing her. She only regretted not sleeping with more of them. And of catching her heart on Etienne.

I arrive at Yvette's a half-hour early, barefaced, dressed in a short pleated skirt and long-sleeved blouse. A girl's idea of being all dressed up, Yvette says as she stands at the door in her own naked face. "You tink we're going to Disneyland?"

I shrug. Sorta.

Yvette huffs about needing more time if she's going to create the right effect for me. It normally takes her an hour for her own face. I need definition, an older outline, she says.

"Mon Dieu, seigneur du ciel," Yvette mutters. Clients like Monsieur Gravelle don't take showgirls shopping so they can feel like child molesters. I like the word showgirl. It's so much better than stripper. "On the other hand," Yvette says, "there's a certain charm to a young woman, *non?"* She mutters back and forth with herself, trying to decide if bringing me is a good idea or not. She's risking a lot, she says.

Monsieur Gravelle is her best client, a museum curator, recently widowed. He's taken her out once a month for nineteen years. To the good places—Holt Renfrew, Ogilvie's, Sparks Street—not those disgusting malls. All he wants is for her to model the clothes, for both of them to be well attended, and for that she gets a dress. She says she could have ten, but she only chooses one. It makes it more fair, Yvette thinks, and suits her sense of dignity. Afterward they dine and dance at the Château.

Now she's arguing against my going again. Monsieur's daughter is my age, for Christ's sake. Hers are even older. What the hell is she doing? She likes me, she says, that's all. Even though I'm kind of raw and unsophisticated. She says I think I'm invincible but that she likes my enthusiasm, all arms and legs on stage. She laughs at me a lot, as if I'm comical. She says

I'm smart and alive in my head, still reaching for other places. I'm different from Emma and Ruby, Yvette tells me. Not mad or sleepy like them. Maybe Yvette wants to save me. Or mother me. She's always trying to boost me up like I'm small in myself. I don't mind it, I just don't want to disappoint her.

I wander through Yvette's home while she makes herself up. The place seems bare. Not cold, but cool. Busts and stuff on pedestals, track lights like in museums, everything glassy and tiled. I stop at the photographs, peering at the two girls with identically placid faces. Yvette's daughters, I guess. I'm surprised at their ordinariness. They're convent-educated, I can tell, with flat things on their heads, what do you call them? Mortarboards.

But the rest of the place remains foreign to me, out of my reach. All the light and whiteness makes me squint and feel incomplete. I sit on a cream leather couch, pressing my knees tightly together. I guess Yvette can see my discomfort. She tells me this whole thing is supposed to be fun.

I hesitate, trying to imagine Yvette's Monsieur. Doesn't she feel weird having someone buy things for her? "You mean do I feel like a prostitute?" Yvette smiles. *Non!* She doesn't sell sex. She gives her attention, her company, she explains. She accepts gifts because she deserves them. Do I think that makes her cheap? No, I blurt out, not wanting to insult her. I tell her she's a lady, a star. Yvette laughs again. "So you approve?" I nod. I've always lived beyond the seams of logic, I've always been able to see beyond the obvious.

But sometimes I feel blurry about moral things, wishing for other people's certainty. I know right from wrong in the big sweep of life, but what I know best is the thing in between, the urgencies of the human heart, its needs and instincts. I like the full gale of internal forces: love, fear, jealousy. To judge such things, to condemn the actions they inspire—I don't do that.

My eyes keep swinging back to the pictures, wanting to know about the girls. About Etienne. I guess I'm pretty obvious. "Dere fadder, 'e was a beautiful man, ooopphh! Dat's what you want to know?"

I nod sheepishly.

"Dat's okay."

I can tell Yvette wants me to know Etienne, the place he'd carved in her; how she craved his coming back alive, not caring what little of him arrived. He could still dance then, she tells me, like you wouldn't believe. Like Fred Astaire, but stronger in the hips. More sexy. And dressed so nicely, even to go to the butcher. He had a big, big heart, soft, like a man should.

Yvette says Etienne loved the opera, that he would cry every Sunday afternoon listening to the radio, holding his squirming girls on his knee, his tears plopping onto their starched dresses. The drinking had stopped his working, erasing him slowly. First it was his looks, then his clothes, then his appetite.

Yvette found work in the clubs then, she'd had to, with Lili St. Cyr. They were big, big shows in beautiful clubs. She'd made good money and been adored.

Then everything changed. The revues got smaller, then disappeared. Yvette stayed on, getting smaller, too. Etienne, didn't like her going but they never quarrelled over it. The booze didn't make him mean. He tried so hard to get free and she tried with him, holding his cold hand in the clinics, paying for the medicines. He died when the youngest one, Sophie, was six.

Yvette had kept her girls in private school after that. And always she'd found enough money to take them for a month to Florida. So it wasn't so bad, eh? I don't answer, can't, afraid I'll sound pitying. Yvette pushes away her ache, refusing to sink into it. "Away *donc*," she says finally. Let's make your face, den see what we can buy you."

It's Yvette's idea to arrive late for Monsieur Gravelle. Only desperate women wait for men, she explains, and only cheap ones wait on the street. We saunter into Holt's slowly, casually. Late. I'm startled by the opulence. The shop is hushed like rich places are, watchful, and full of willowy clerks and stubby, fussing matrons. Yvette tells me the wives of prime ministers shop here. I imagine the hawk eyes of a floorwalker on me.

Monsieur Gravelle approaches us gingerly, kisses Yvette on both cheeks. He doesn't look anything like Sugar's Old Man, not grey and sunken in. He's fat like the professor in *Blue Angel,* bearded and balding and overly buttoned, with shiny fob and watch. A gentleman, I think. Something out of the last century. I almost curtsy when Yvette introduces us.

"Ah, the new ecdysiast," he exclaims. Now I know how to pronounce it. His hand is pudgy and wet.

Monsieur Gravelle is well-to-do but there's something haunted about him, I think, deprived even, as though he'd spent his childhood in some mahogany-panelled room without anyone to talk to. I follow mutely as he and Yvette lock arms and head for the dress department. Like they could be my parents.

Yvette moves expertly from rack to rack, feeling the fabric, holding the gowns in front of herself, whispering playfully to Monsieur Gravelle. I mimic her as best I can, not so much looking at the garments as hiding behind them. The clerks smell money and hover, picking at Yvette's choices with sharpened fingernails. One even speaks to me but I won't answer back. Yvette tells me to sit with Monsieur Gravelle as she disappears into the changing room.

I squirm as the Monsieur asks me simple questions that aren't simple at all. Am I working my way through college? No. Did I study dance, ballet perhaps? I lie, borrowing from the stories Emma's told me, inserting the word pointes liberally. Then what did I think of Nureyev's Toronto performance? I struggle for an opinion. But what about Mohammed Ali trouncing Frazier last week? I coax him. It sure killed business at the club but wasn't it great? Monsieur Gravelle smiles weakly.

Mostly the Monsieur fixes his attention on Yvette as she models various evening dresses. He directs her eagerly, to bend, walk, twirl, his big, white face growing pink and wet. Yvette plays his excitement expertly, making him the centre of attention, rallying the clerks to get him cake and coffee. A single blue vein swells up on his temple, throbbing. Neither seems to notice the matrons whispering or the store pulling into itself and staring. I feel small and furious. The same clerks who'd fluttered around us are now bent at each other's ears, raising eyebrows at Yvette. Hypocrites! I stare back sourly.

All afternoon Monsieur and Yvette fuss and primp until finally the selection is down to two gowns: the tight green taffeta and the billowing yellow organza.

There's a last flurry as the clerks mutter their elastic opinions and Yvette and Monsieur deliberate in deep and secret whispers. I don't think they really want to make a choice, they don't want the game to end. It *is* a game, a *pas de deux*—beautiful and choreographed, maybe even a form of love. Intimate but sexless. Inciting the senses. Who could understand older people?

Finally Yvette decides to take the green taffeta. The Monsieur claps his hands.

"Man has his will but woman has her way," he booms. I stare blankly. "Oliver Wendell Holmes." Uh huh.

But what about me, Yvette cajoles the Monsieur. What should they get me? They all turn their eyes on me. I'm numb by now, pale and tired. It is their sport, after all. But they insist and I drag along behind them,

examining racks of clothes and counters of silk, perfume and jewelry.

It's silly, I know, but I decide on a pair of white
bobby socks. Yvette and the old man are disappointed
but it's my way of retaliating against the place. They're
only two ninety-five, hardly enough for a commission,
and when the sales girl looks down her nose, I ask her
to gift-wrap them. Yvette smiles approvingly.

Miss,
Please give me your phone number. Or your
address. Do you mind? I like you very much.
I came from BANGKOK, THAILAND. I will
waiting for your give me the answer.
 Yours friend, Mr. B. Kum-Qot

Eden hurts my nose this early in the morning. It stinks
in here. The other girls have arrived already but I don't
see Ric. Not yet. Not that I care. He's cautious with
me now, nervous and circling. Afraid maybe I'll tell
everyone how different he is in private. I try not to be
alone with him anymore. He watches me sometimes
with sorry eyes, I think. Wanting to finish things. I
don't let him.

Today's the press conference, the day the big
American star arrives. The room is tense this early; the
girls curl away from the light, squinting, without their
nighttime flush.

Sugar asks if I'm hungry and offers cold toast. She's nice to me now, always leaning into me, whispering secrets. Like they're a gift. She even replaced my Dietrich costume. Anyway, we're even, and everyone knows it. Even Emma, who doesn't mention that night until now. "You sure have her trained," Emma croaks. "So how the fuck was he?" I burn red under her swollen eyes. "Amazing," I lie.

I don't tell her Ric hurried into me, fumbling and blind like a boy. Or that my heart caught on him and tore. I wanted him badly, like food. He was shades of light I hadn't lived, all the sixties in a single brilliant burst. I wanted him to teach me to love like artists do. To live with me, maybe, in Greenwich Village or Yorkville, in bed all day eating tea and oranges that come all the way from China.

Ric was the oldest man I'd ever been with and I'd wanted to grow wise and womanly. But he wouldn't say my name out loud, my real one, or look me in the eyes so we could blur together. I hovered outside my own body unclaimed. No Leonard Cohen poems, no words of worship and fidelity anchoring me to him. We stayed ordinary. And I'd cried, stupid like a girl, at the cold, turned back of romance. I scratched my hurt into a poem, thinking I'd give it to him. I didn't.

Small-backed, string bean,
Carolina man
Your love is a trick.

But Emma doesn't know about the bad part. I need to keep my lustre for the big morning ahead. I've been imagining the American star for weeks: her costumes and routines. We all think being American is bigger and brighter than being us, all sparkly and leggy like Las Vegas.

Johnny's told us she was coming to Canada because of the energy crisis. All I know about the oil shortage is from TV news: snaky lineups at American gas stations and herds of Arabs flapping around like nuns in habits. What that has to do with Rae Darren, Miss Nude World, coming to Eden is fuzzy to me but the press conference is supposed to explain it.

"Hey, hey, big day," Worm shouts, bouncing into the dressing room. "Lots of press guys down there. Gonna be famous." His cheeriness is cold like a shower. "Shut up, you moron," Emma snaps. She's puffed up with her allergies, cranky. "It's so early it 'urts," Yvette groans. I help her with her stockings, I like to, rolling them up and pulling them over her feet. Abe saunters in.

Everyone is pissed off at Johnny for forcing us here. He said we had to show up for the press conference and dress sexy or he'd fine us. Yvette says it's a sad thing when professional dancers have to be waitresses. But I don't mind—I want to be here. Yvette asks Abe what he thinks. He shrugs and says *comme ci, comme ça*. It's what those clowns down there want. Market forces. Don't it stink? Then Abe hands out bagels like he's making things up to us. Yvette tousles his hair. At least we're safe with Abe, never having to put on hard faces or make ourselves small for him.

Sugar wants to know how you get to be Miss Nude World. Ruby too. She says it can't be Miss World if you can't count in Muslim women. Right? Or Red China. Abe smiles and says we ought to get her for libel. She's only Miss Nude Half the World. We're laughing our tits off when Fat-Ass Gladys comes into the room, barking, "Let's go, let's go. Rae Darren's going to be here any minute and she wants privacy. And grab those cheese trays, girls. And be nice to the press!"

"Kiss my ass!" We turn back to our conversation. Sugar's heard Rae Darren's got rhinestones on everything. Emma holds her hands away from her chest and says she's got silicone boobs out to there. I don't know what silicone is. Fake boobs, she explains.

But how? "They either inject you or they cut you open and stuff it in." Ruby says you explode if you're near fire so you can't smoke.

Finally, Abe says it's time to go and tugs us out of the room. I grab my tray of cheese balls and crackers. "This is it, baby," Emma groans. "The national fucking press corps."

It's like a high-school lockerroom down at the front rows. About fifty guys in suits and jackets are milling around with pencils and cameras, laughing and slapping each other like teammates. I pass around the food and act interested. Somebody from the local paper asks what I think of the energy crisis. I tell him I'm too young to have an energy crisis. He thinks that's funny and writes it down. Does he want my name, I ask. Nah. Somebody else wants to take my picture but Johnny tells him to save it for the real star.

A clap of thunder booms through the club, vibrating against the walls: *"Ladies and gentlemen of the press, direct from New Orleans, Eden is proud to present Miss Nude World, Rae Darren."* A strobe light flashes. Something moves on stage. Milky white light spills on a long black box. It's a...it's a coffin. Drums beat loud, fast, white hands push open the coffin lid. A flash of light and smoke billows into the air. A woman emerges in a black cape, her hands reaching up through the smoke. *"Ladies and gentlemen,* on the occasion of her first Canadian engagement, please welcome Rae Darren."

Wow, a double intro. The reporters jump to their feet, applauding and hooting. "Aaalllright," Ruby hollers.

Rae Darren's tight leather dress blinks with red and white rhinestones. For forty minutes she owns the stage and my mouth goes dry from staying open. Sugar's face is pinched and worried. Especially near the end when Rae grabs hold of the flaming batons. It's incredible. With a single intake of breath she blows out a long red tail of fire, roaring and red. "Bravo," I scream, we scream.

When Rae reemerges she's on top of the coffin, smiling through long white fangs. Blood dribbles down her body, mixing with the sweat. Smoke starts pouring from the floor and curls into the air. Rae pulls off her bra and stands there naked. Finished. Everybody's cheering, yelling, stomping. I try getting a good look at her but smoke's swallowing her. She reappears in a black cape, bowing. Johnny rushes on stage. "Let's hear it for Eden's biggest star...."

The cheering goes on and on. Johnny keeps waving his hands, screaming at everybody to quiet down so Miss Nude World can answer questions. Rae Darren sits down and takes off her cape. We all pull in our breath. Her boobs are huge, misshapen. It's unbelievable. They don't move; they just stick out like tin cans, hard and stiff. *"That* is silicone," Emma whispers. The press men crawl through the dark, over each other, aiming their flashbulbs, firing, reloading, shouting out questions. Miss Nude World answers clearly, unblinkingly. I feel sorry for her—I don't know why.

Rae Darren talks in a soft southern whisper. She explains that she's a professional traveller, like a salesman or truck driver. She says President Nixon should give people like her special licences so they can get more gas to get to their jobs. American strippers are even organizing a march on Washington. She's come up here because it's easier to buy gas and because the speed limits are higher.

"How much is your salary here in Canada?" a reporter shouts. "Twelve hundred a week, U.S." Our mouths drop. "Do you know you've got a bigger crowd here today than External Affairs Minister

Mitchell Sharp and the Canadian Labour Congress?"
Rae smiles demurely. She's flattered, she says. "Now if
any of you'd care to take a press kit, there are posters
and matchbooks by the door. Please help yourself."
The reporters stampede.

But Emma won't be thawed. It's all hype, she
gripes in her froggy voice, it's not a real protest. I don't
care. It's a great show. I'd love to be Rae Darren. So
would Emma, I bet. I race down the stairs and into the
swirl around Rae.

I've only been close to fame once, when Prime
Minister John Diefenbaker came to my grandmother's
church. People got real close, squashing him, but my
grandmother pushed through, shoving me ahead like
an offering. His big head leaned down at me and I felt
clean and warm in his attention. I want to get up close
to Rae Darren so she can give that feeling back to me.

The other girls are zipping through the crowd too.
Ruby gushes when she reaches Rae Darren. "Totally
far out!" she says. "You're amazing."

Sugar elbows in and congratulates Rae on the fire
breathing, as if she's some damn aficionado. Then she
blabs about her nude skydiving. Rae Darren listens
patiently but she's just being nice. She turns finally
and smiles at me. "It's an honour to meet you," I sput-
ter, shrinking into my Sunday school manners. "I'm
one of the dancers here." She gives me a big hug. I
float into that big pillowy sensation of contentment.

For two weeks Eden sparkles like a Las Vegas
nightclub. Rae Darren erases our shabby everyday.

Thousands of new, high-class customers pack the place, bringing wives and girlfriends. It's strange seeing so many women. The men behave better but more timidly. They all come for Rae's big-time show. And for her breasts. People here haven't ever seen silicone and Rae's got plenty of it, in both sets of cheeks too. I hear their whisperings, the jokes and horror. Husbands and wives leave clutching each other, assured in their ordinary beauty. It bugs me.

Rae's a professional, not like us. I see her working before shows and between them, selling photographs and doing interviews. One morning she pickets the American embassy while we are still in bed. Emma says she's not an artist at all but a publicity hound, that she's turning stripping into a business. I don't know if that's good or bad. There's a certainty about Rae, though, a centre of gravity I envy. I don't always know what I'm doing here. Sometimes I think it's about barenakedness and being wild, other times it's feelings and ideas. It's never been about money or career; I don't really see the future or me in it. I guess I sort of drift, pulled by the force of the strongest sensation. It's never bothered me till now.

The other girls are surprised they like Rae. She's not the Hollywood snob we thought she'd be. She acts like one of us, spreading her friendship evenly. She smokes hash with Ruby and shares costume tips with Sugar. She even listens to Emma's rants about American imperialism and corruption. Emma won't shut up about the U.S. embargo on Cuba and how

Fidel Castro taught all the prostitutes to read, and about Watergate. Rae can see into her deeper goodness, I guess. Emma's kind but it's mostly for people in far-off places.

Rae's got tons of stories about the American strippers and my imagination swells. They call themselves showgirls down there, which is pretty professional. Rae rhymes off the names of the big acts as though we're supposed to know them. Only Yvette does, some. "Carol Doda! *Hasti*, I remember 'er from Frisco." Her knowing adds some needed lustre to our ranks.

The way Rae tells it, there are heaps of strippers in the States with catchy names you can't forget. Like Eva Knieval, the professional stunt girl who does a strip show with a motorcycle. Or Charity Ball, the blonde *Playboy* centrefold with the shower act. Of course, mention that magazine and Sugar has to brag about being a bunny in the Montreal club. See, look, she chirps, she can even remember the "dip." Sugar lowers her body, chest first. She means dipstick, Emma snickers.

Rae says American strippers travel a lot, crisscrossing the States with roadies and show vans. Sometimes with their own bodyguards. They all have professional photographers and book through agents and make big money. For two brief weeks I pretend that world is mine.

I make an American Thanksgiving dinner for Rae and the girls, in honour of her last show. We don't usually go to each other's houses, though Sugar keeps saying she's going to invite us to her new place. I'm nervous. I imagine myself as the goodwill ambassador between American and Canadian strippers. Or show-girls.

My bachelor apartment is cold and bare. I don't have chairs, or even a table. I prop an old door up on milk crates and throw on a tablecloth. With pillows and candles the room looks almost biblical, like the Last Supper. I roast a twenty-two pound turkey cautiously—I had to ask the butcher how to cook it.

My place looks great, the girls look great in candlelight. We eat and drink and burn chunks of hash, laughing at stupid club jokes: "How many strippers does it take to screw in a light bulb? Screwing's extra; you only paid to watch."

Deep in the night we grow soft as children, our limbs long and lax and spread over each other. Touching casually in the way I love, tangled together. A low rumbling of words begins, Yvette's stories about the old burlesque: the Victory, Gayety, the Toronto Casino. We sit at her feet, content as disciples.

She tells us again about the B girls in Montreal, how they worked the Main on St. Laurent and in the cabarets around Bon Secours Market. They were awful places she says, she didn't like mixing with the customers. But the big, big shows, they were incredible, she enthuses, rolling their names in her mouth like candy.

"Glamorous Margie Hart, very sexy. A teaser. Georgia Sodern, de shaker, Rosita Royce and 'er trained doves. But Lili St. Cyr was de queen."

I love this part best. I can recite all the words before Yvette can. *Lili was no shaker or grinder...*

"Lili was no shaker or grinder," Yvette explains.

...she was a fantasist, an illusionist....

"She was a fantasist, an illusionist. Acting out Sampson and Delilah, Romeo and Juliet. In flowing costumes made of silk and taffeta."

She could make you fly away with her....

"She could make you fly away wit her," Yvette says softly. "De woman came more to de shows dan de man."

The men. Tell us about the men, the girls plead. Yvette throws back her head and laughs throatily. Rich ones, she purrs. "Dey give you airplane tickets to France for a weekend. Or de Mardi Gras. Sometimes dey want to buy de woman a retirement business, a store or canteen.

"There were gangsters, too, from Chicago and New York, from Miami. But they were clean and polite then. Gentlemen." Yvette's voice trails off here, leaving a space to dream in. I wait for the finish line she tags on to every story. "Dat's it and dat's all," she laughs.

But I don't want to come back. Why can't it be like that again? Why not? Why not, we all chime. "Things are different," Yvette says curtly. I wait for a better answer. She throws up her hands. "It's changed, okay? Dey don't want shows no more."

But she's wrong, I tell her. They're jamming the place to see Rae. They love her show. Yvette's eyes flash me a warning. "You tink it's just for fun. For...."

"Artistic expression," Sugar trumpets drunkenly.

"NO!" Rae's voice stings like a slap. She's tugging at the buttons of her blouse, telling us to look, telling us what she had to do to go from making four hundred a week to twelve hundred. "Feel them, go ahead," she says to me. I don't want to touch them. "Go on."

They are hard as rock. I pull away quickly.

Rae's voice is thin now. "They said I'd never feel it but the sacs keep moving. They hurt." Yvette takes her hand. "God damn it, goddammit," Rae repeats, the words getting mangled in her throat. She's had four operations and she's got to keep paying the bastards. I feel red with shame for being so stupid. For not catching the warnings. I stroke her hair, her back. The girls move in close, touching parts of her. Pulling her pain out like slivers. We linger in a heap until her tears run dry. Rae wipes her face then smiles weakly.

"Hell, at least with these babies I'll never drown," she says.

We claim our laughter like sinking men claim lifeboats.

I love the exhilaration before a set, the cold terror that moves through me. I love being afraid and riding my fear to the edge of myself and then in. My new show makes the feeling stronger, makes me almost fall over with dread. I've finally given in to Johnny and Gladys's demands for a little girl act. But my Red Riding Hood isn't cute or sexy like they want. I've been moving beyond my twirliness, becoming more definite and sure, like Rae. I've been making eye contact with the audience and cracking jokes: "Don't applaud, just throw money." Emma calls my Riding Hood show twisted. It's her highest compliment.

I bounce on stage to tinny, kiddy music and prance around with my basket and my red cape. Some of the men laugh right away, others look impatient. I like how their faces harden, knowing that I will soften them. "Don't ya think I'm woman enough?" I holler, and their sternness wavers. I begin the first song shyly, with girlish poses, soothing the men with my vulnerability. They start to relax. Then the music turns dark, Hitchcock's TV theme, and I pretend to wander through the woods. I jump off the stage and skip through the crowd, startling the men with my closeness. Some pull away from me, embarrassed, others lean in closer. Sometimes someone tries to feel me or pinch me, but I swat him hard with my storybook. "Get your dirty old man hands off me," I shriek dramatically, even if he hasn't touched me, and he shrinks into the darkness with his guilt. I hand out goodies from my basket: coloured condoms or little bags of salt with saltpeter labels I've stuck on. Sometimes it's pictures of men's underwear that I've cut out from a catalogue. "Wanna see something sexy?" I ask. Then I climb back on stage to start the strip.

I ham up my clumsiness, tugging at my cape and getting twisted underneath it. I pop out grinning and the audience applauds my victory, surrendering to my show and the humour. Once it does, I change my role, turning cat-like, soft on my feet, rolling my limbs in their sockets as I slink into the chair on the stage and curl into the classic stocking number. Except I'm not wearing stockings, just the bobby socks I bought with Yvette. I sit poised and arch-backed on the edge of the seat, running my hand down the length of my leg, looking out with pouting lips and half-closed lids. The skeptics start to melt. I cross my legs and reach down, rolling off my sock slowly, hooking it over my heel.

Then I stop, pretending the sock is stuck. I yank at it, pulling, pulling, forcing my foot above my head, behind my head like a contortionist, lurching back, falling off the chair, rolling on the floor. The regulars howl but the first-timers don't know what to do and wonder if I need help, if I have broken something, if I might be a little insane. I flail around, all kneecaps and elbows, trying to unsnag myself. It's so ridiculous, I clench my jaw shut not to laugh. Finally I stick a leg out from my balled up limbs and dangle it at the front row. I tap my foot on someone's head or shoulders, signaling him to pull the sock off. It's better when the men are embarrassed or offended, when they pretend not to see me, or push me away—then my foot creeps back, stroking, tickling, bending forward in a little wave of hello. My five naked toes wriggle under a tight white spotlight and two hundred men watch: "Are you hot and bothered yet?" I love the fun of it, the shared joke, the warm circle of humanness, and the razor's edge of humour that can turn on me. It's dangerous playing with people's expectations, but performance is like a military manoeuvre; the idea is to ambush the other side, to keep them surprised.

After my foot dance I reward the audience with clichés: unzipping my frilly dress shyly, pulling out an arm, then the other, holding the dress against my chest, hunching around it, hiding, slipping it off finally to reveal my ruby red rhinestone bra and panties. The regulars know I'm kidding and scream out encouragements—a smirking conspiracy that confounds the new guys. Then I pick up the pace: "Hey there, Little Red Riding Hood" the music booms, "You sure are looking good," the audience sings along. I let down my hair and then I do a running front flip, landing on my feet, spinning my head on my neck so my long hair flies, whirling and twirling, breaking into a sweat, into hard, tight muscles. "The girl who cried wolf," Emma screams from the balcony. I pull my bra off quickly, almost imperceptibly, sneaking into my nakedness. It is almost beside the point. The audience begins to blur now as I go furiously into myself, feeling every tendon stretch, every searing breath, and the air on my wet skin. It's a primitive loosening, intensely religious, a prayer said out loud in a roomful of strangers. Sometimes I peek out and see the men watching me, mesmerized.

For the next song, I move in slow motion, in a series of freeze-frame poses—an outstretched leg, arm, an arched spine—creating long, straight lines and cascading motions, making beautiful, balletic symmetry. In the last song I put on a long frilly negligee and spin in twenty billowing yards of fabric, fluttering it around myself like wings, like wind, playing in the spotlight, letting its beam caress me, chase me, claim me in a silhouette. After all these months, I still have trouble remembering to unclip my G-string, then I leap across the stage in a last burst, pressing the fabric against my skin, revealing nothing in my motion, just face, hands, feet. I hold my body straight, balancing on the ball of one foot, spinning, spinning, spinning, reaching my arms into the darkness above me, wet and tired, not naked and small but swollen in myself, fiercely proud. Complete.

The men are cheering. I love it.

CHAPTER 4

Sylvester's Day in Court

I feel like a mouse in a cat's house. Sugar has invited

me home finally and we go to the back by the river. I

watch her kneeling in the sun, her body greased with

lotion and shiny as glazed ham. She pinches off the

rose heads with pointed, graceful hands, aware of her-

self, of the constant eyes she imagines fixed on her.

Never really alone. She's the most beautiful girl I've

ever seen.

Sugar's more fragile sober, humming nervously in herself. She does have inner doubts, a need to account for her worth. She counts her accomplishments, measuring them out loud. She's done well with the garden and the house, she says.

I remember her wanting to buy this house by the river. She'd read somewhere that movie stars bought country estates. I bet she'd gone to the bank with half-lowered eyes and her best Marilyn Monroe imitation. The manager must have lingered attentively but he wouldn't loan money to—how did he put it?—free-lancers. Sugar rented instead.

The house is fallen on its haunches and tilting on the bank of the Rideau River. Still, Sugar claims it frantically, cooing at Ric, even now, to hoist it up. She's applied the full force of her will on the old place, consulting magazines, sewing curtains, peeling off wallpaper. She'll live happily ever after here, she says, raising children, loving Ric, basking in celebrity. All her perfect selves will blossom: cook, gardener, lover, artist. Maybe she'll even stop drinking.

Sugar's genius is imitation, not invention. She changes herself externally, wearing other identities until she becomes them. She's always trying to become someone else, someone better. To be superior, we all think. Perhaps it's only to be worthy. She's always talking about opportunity lurking around the next corner. Maybe she has to be ready.

I don't understand her optimism. She's told me she grew up an orphan, but not orphaned enough, living among her mother's family, passed around like bad news. No one knew her father. Her mother was spoken of in low clicking sounds at night among the adults. Her relations were stern religious people with a cranky God. But when she prayed it wasn't to their bruised Christ but to the goddess she imagined her mother to be. Growing into beauty must have antagonized the laws of their justice. Her aunts were especially unforgiving. And stingy. There was no money left for prom dresses, Sugar says through pursed lips, for pom-poms or trips to camp where her cousins went.

Somehow Sugar took possession of her beauty, watching herself in the eyes of the boys, in the reflections of the shop windows and the rearview mirrors of parked cars, assuring herself of her worthiness, of the fact she existed. Perhaps her ambition came from her certain effect on men. She avoids younger ones, preferring the gravity of their fathers and grandfathers, like the Old Man. Or the eagerness of foreigners like Ric.

Over the years Sugar untangled her family's whisperings, deciding on the reasons for her mother's leaving. She ran away with an American, to California. She's probably someone famous in Hollywood, Sugar thinks. I've seen her study movie magazines as if they were family albums, maybe looking for her mother's face. It's a secret thing she does, a last thread to the lost years. As faithful an act as crossing herself.

Sugar meanders through her stories all afternoon, strangely outside her own experience, as though she's narrating someone else's life. Time is not a continuous line for Sugar, but a series of freeze-frames, like pictures in a book. What she remembers fiercely are efforts of will. And her own starring role.

Sugar recalls pushing herself into the TV auditions and getting the job dancing on *Top Ten. People still ask for her autograph.* Or heaving herself out of the Piper and fluttering to the earth naked. *Only a single news crew covers that.* Or posing with her snake for *Playboy. She is in negotiations with a famous New York photographer.*

These are the victories that anchor in Sugar's mind, assuring her of stardom. And of my undivided attention. She pauses in her imaginary glow of adoration, its halo around her head. There's such a complicated falseness to her beauty, a stinging insecurity. Fear trickles through Sugar, deep down and animal. I can feel it coming off her. She thinks she's being watched.

Sugar walks around the hedges and down the length of the yard to the river. No one is there. She is afraid and she doesn't know why. Sugar laughs at herself and tells me she's still getting used to living in the country. Or maybe it's having another woman around that makes her jumpy. Sugar thinks women are treacherous, unreliable, out to get her, to steal from her. I know she thinks that of me, which is why I'm surprised I'm sitting here.

Sugar has never really forgiven me for that night with Ric, for the months of effort she's had to make to win him back. The house is part of her rehabilitation.

And the flowers, the quilts, the softer, homier self she's found in *Redbook*. Maybe she wants to show me, to fortify her claim, like a wolf pissing around its territory. I know she's worked hard at all this. Sugar hates reading anything but celebrity biographies. Her mind prefers pictures and films. But she's been forcing herself through the pages of these women's magazines, finding wifely women to imitate so she can convince Ric of her remade love and worth. She's even stepped into the smoky light of AA. She cried there, she says, remembering the beautiful spectacle she made of herself.

Wound all through the day is this feeling that Sugar's trying to tell me something, trying to get me to have a firmer, better opinion of her, maybe even to forgive her. It's as if she's afraid of something shadowy in her mind, of what she's becoming. I think she's less complicated when she's drunk.

Dear Mme Fonda,
I send you best regards and good wishes. I enjoy seeing your performance every day last week. On the outside the sign says the dirtiest show in town. I do not believe it is dirty. Instead it is beautiful, as the girls. Your show is very natural, interesting and kind for men.

If it is your pleasure I will introduce myself. I am seeing you every Thursday after my water colouring. I am an artist in my retreat. I wish you continue strength and happiness.

My salutations, M. Savard

I expected the room to be darker and striped with venetian blind light the way it is on *Perry Mason*. To stare down at me. But the courtroom is bright as a drug store, full of people coming and going like shoppers. I sit at the front with the lawyer, trying to make out the order of things. I'm not as afraid as I thought I'd be. Or as important.

I still don't know who finked on me. Maybe it was the weird numerology guy who kept waiting for me outside the club. He'd wanted me to change my name because the letters in mine were unlucky when he'd added them up. I finally had to complain to Abe about him. It could have been Sugar or even Johnny. He liked the publicity. It had to be someone who knew me because when the cops came they asked for me by name. My real name. At first I thought they were looking for another dead girl, like the drowned one last time. I still remember the photograph of that swollen blue face. But they said they were arresting me.

I felt bad right away, sick, as if I'd been hit in the stomach. I think the cops felt bad too, especially the taller one. He talked really softly and told me to stop shaking; he wasn't taking me to jail. His name was P.C. Pearson. The fat one was bored or disgusted. He wouldn't look me, as though I were dirty.

P.C. Pearson took me into Johnny's office and said there'd been a complaint about an obscene theatrical performance. They'd watched the show themselves and thought it was borderline. Emma came down and huffed and puffed about public servants being paid to think dirty. It didn't help.

It makes me small and angry, knowing people think I'm obscene. I've been working on some new routines, building up my comedy. The puppet show is part of that. It's a green hand puppet with a long red tongue. I call him Sylvester—I feel stupid saying his name to the cops. I do this thing at the end of the show where the puppet tries to get into my G-string and I smack him away. He's pretty persistent, grabbing my arm, biting my leg. I finally stop him dead by tying his tongue to his head with my G-string. It's a big hit. Everyone laughs, except cops, I guess.

P.C. Pearson wanted to see I.D. I lied and told him it had been stolen. He said he had to charge me and that I'd have to go to court. He said it as if he was sorry. I was scared, not about jail but about Juvenile Hall, about being whacked back into girlhood and losing my life here. I couldn't go back there. I couldn't. But Johnny was excited, as if being arrested was good. He said he'd get me a lawyer, a really great one. And not to worry 'cause I'd get off.

I only believed Johnny when Abe confirmed it was true. He said he'd look out for me and not to be afraid. Putting names on my feelings made me want to cry.

The next day the newspaper had a third of a page about the arrest. It had my name and address too. I didn't want that numerologist knowing where I lived. And I didn't want my family finding out what I did. They thought I worked for a dentist. But not anymore.

Things got exaggerated after that. The girls acted as if I were a hero fighting off the straight world, especially Emma. They claimed my arrest like it belonged to them. I let them. I enjoyed the attention.

Sugar looked scared when I took her place in the lineup. I was the star for a couple of weeks, "The Girl Too Hot for Vice." The club gummed up with new faces wanting to see what the fuss was about. Johnny smiled like a hyena. Even Skyway Cable called.

The man on the phone talked as though he was my best friend. When I got to the studio he asked me to describe the show, to tell him how I got sexually turned on. They were dirty, sweaty questions and I didn't want to talk that way on television. Rae Darren wouldn't talk like that. There's a power I have when I'm on the stage. I don't have it as much in real life but I do with an audience. I reached for it now, pushing him back with it, making a space. I talked about rights and artistic freedom like Emma would have. I could tell he was mad but the cameras had trapped him.

It took nine months for my case to get to court. P.C. Pearson kept wanting my I.D. and I kept stalling. He knew I was underage but he didn't tell. He kept coming to my home, dropping in unexpectedly, all through winter and spring, sometimes for no reason. My new roommates didn't like it. Every visit was preceded by three or four minutes of terror as we stashed our dope and hid the hookah.

P.C. wasn't his real name. It stood for police constable. After I learned that I still called him P.C. I liked him. He seemed nervous, as if he wanted to say something to me but couldn't. Maybe he liked me. Once when I was taking a drunk friend home in his Jaguar, I got stopped for driving without a licence. I called P.C. and the cop let me go.

P.C. called me by my real name and always wanted to know why I was a stripper. He would wince apologetically and he'd feel small for asking. I saw that look on lots of men. They didn't like stripping but they did like me. It was hard for them to straighten that out in their minds. I never had an answer that explained it well enough. Usually I said it was because I liked stripping or it was fun. But it's so many other things they can't understand. Girls are different, more bendable in their minds; my girlfriends don't strip but they don't judge, either. Men's minds are caught in a web of morality. Things are good or bad, right or wrong. Never in the middle places where women live.

Johnny's lawyer is fat and grey and important. I met him last week, just five days before the court date. He didn't seem to care about anything but winning. He talked a lot and when he listened he wanted me to hurry. He told me to dress demurely, and did I know what that meant? And to keep my eyes lowered and my mouth shut. I nodded, letting myself free-fall into his hands and Johnny's.

Johnny sent me to his wholesaler friend Max for an outfit. I was grateful for his bargains but I wouldn't sleep with him. I got new white shoes from Vachek the shoeman—half price, he said, for fighting the Philistines. Whoever they were.

I come into court dressed all in white in a skirt and jacket. Looking like Suzanne Pleshette. The girls sit in the back and wave. Yvette drops her chin approvingly and Abe is there too, winking. At first I feel small up front, beside the lawyer. P.C. is here and smiles in a way no one else can see. He testifies, describing my show surgically but in a dull, detached way, as though it hasn't made an impact on his morals. I thank him with my eyes.

I try keeping my mind sharp, following the legal words, but they ricochet across the courtroom. Everyone's speaking but me, raising their voices, pouncing on each other's arguments. The lawyer yells at the judge to take a look at my face, a good look, as if my jawline can prove my innocence. His Honour lowers his eyes slowly in my direction as if he can't see me. *He can't see me.*

I pull out of my mind abruptly, tearing clean from my usual thoughts, my old perceptions used up. Maybe this trial isn't about goodness, just like stripping's not really about sex. Maybe justice is about being important, about wearing nice clothes, selling newspapers, getting Johnny publicity. Maybe it's about the judge watching the clerk in the miniskirt.

The world is tilting differently, dangerously. These new thoughts sting as much as people thinking I'm dirty and obscene. I'm not. I am not.

After an hour the judge slams down a heap of paper and bellows that the case is dismissed. Johnny and the lawyer leap up and hug like actors. The girls hoot from the back. I swagger the way I'm supposed to but I don't mean it.

Abe is watching me with a reassuring look on his face. None of this is about me, he says. I guess I know that but it doesn't stop the hollowness I feel inside, the wincing sense of loss. I want to get back to my own life. To definiteness.

CHAPTER 5

Riding Hood
and the Wolves

For months Emma jabs at Johnny's ego with the sharpness of a pin, trying to deflate him. Johnny's swelled up with the trial publicity, calling himself an entrepreneur and a freedom of speech advocate now. New friends cram into his office every night, rich guys, hard and shiny as the gold and diamonds on their hands, pulled by Johnny's celebrity—"like flies to shit," Emma says. But I like the foreign glitter of Johnny's friends, especially Bill the restaurant owner, the one Emma calls "Slug." Boy, did her face curdle last night when she saw me leave with him.

I curl alongside Emma in the dark by Johnny's office, feeling into the raw sound of male voices. They're CFL players tonight, stump-necked American boys sniffling with their wet coke noses. One of them is bragging about getting a blow job from a fifteen year old. "Probably his sister," Emma says sourly. Then she heads downstairs for her show.

Emma's been doing this set a lot lately, just to bother Johnny, I think. She ricochets around the stage with a prickly fierceness, pulling off all her clothes in the first song, then beginning the low, slow rant, the Sylvia Plath poetry—firing words like shrapnel, dumbfounding the men. Especially the ones in Johnny's office. "What the hell is that?" they ask.

"You do not do, you do not do
Any more, black shoe..."

The poem drones on and the audience jeers but Emma doesn't flinch. She stands naked in their spray with her hands on her hips, spitting more words, laughing at them. It's an act of war and the men always lose, but they'll come back, bringing friends to continue the combat. Emma knows it's the reason Johnny doesn't fire her.

It *is* a mystery to Johnny how Emma pulls in the customers, a sore that chafes his maleness. "Damn bitch reminds me of my first wife," I hear him tell the football players. "Mouthy and competitive. Arguing all the...." The other men's snickers feel wet and dirty.

The girls in Eden like the ball players, going flimsy and toothy around them, wanting to rub themselves against the men's lustre. Even Emma felt sorry for them at first, saying they were poor men, accidentally lifted above themselves. Pathetic. Now she thinks they've grown brutish and bulging like apes in their privilege, imagining us girls as their private harem.

"Fuck 'em," Emma thinks. She's not going to cower to their expectations. "Little fucking mice men, like soft-pawed, stupid Lennie in Steinbeck's novel. Killing things they love. Squishing them so hard that breathing stops."

Emma says she knows about suffocation and the strangling grip of privilege. She grew up a surgeon's daughter behind the leafy gauze of perfect lawns and private schools, in frantic pretense, gulping for air.

Emma's told me about words disappearing through her childhood, said but not heard, or just stuck in her mouth so they made a lump and hurt. No wonder she has trouble breathing. When her mother tried to erase her by giving her clothes to Goodwill, words spewed out of Emma and never stopped. Emma says that's when she made a space for herself.

I imagine her sharpening like a blade in that space, growing hostile and outrageous, forcing herself across every border, into every forbidden act—wounding herself as much as anyone else. It's what brought her to Eden the first time, dragging the frat boys behind her.

Emma remembers a blur of women that first night, thinly spirited, anonymous. She'd been bored, she said. But the force of gravity shifted when an older woman came on stage, maybe it was Yvette, she couldn't be sure, but the stripper had a confidence that made Emma smart. She'd been fearless, daring the audience to look at her, startling Emma with her intelligence. And possibilities.

Emma came back to Eden after spring semester, pulling herself on stage as timidly as the others. Wearing the same clichés: arched back, stuck out tits, coy bending—where do we learn it? When that skin fell off she became herself, inventing acts that proclaimed herself, yelling out poetry to make the men squirm.

"And a love of the rack and the screw.
And I said I do, I do..."

Emma's words rumble under Johnny's friends, making them fidget. They call her a dyke again, and Johnny laughs as if he's hearing it for the first time. "So what is she doing here?" someone asks. That shuts Johnny up.

"There's a stake in your fat black heart
And the villagers never liked you."

The remark thuds inside him. Johnny's embarrassed, I can tell, withering under the disapproval. "Fuck her," he says, setting his hate against Emma, like a trap, I bet. Waiting to get her.

Emma thumps past the office on her way up the stairs, grinning at the men belligerently, goading them. Then she empties her rage onto us. Emma is fuming about Johnny's friends—grunts she calls them, telling us we're stupid for liking them. Emma's aiming her fury at me; she's still angry about seeing me with

Bill last night. Bill's all right even if he is Johnny's friend. At least he's not a football player.

"For chrissakes, I grew up in Forest Hill," Emma sneers. "Do you know what that means?" It's a stupid thing to say. Careless. Sugar snickers, "Emma, the private school girl. So much richer than the rest of us."

"I know this shit about power, that's what it means."

"Uh huh. So?" Ruby clucks. Emma fixes her eyes on me. "Don't you ever listen to those grunts, what they say about us? Don't you care?"

"Not really," I shrug.

"They think we're whores."

"They do not," Ruby huffs. Yvette raises her eyebrow like a question mark. "They take us out," Ruby sputters. "We share their dope. We all get laid. What's the big deal?" Emma shakes her head wearily as if she's talking to a mental case. "They don't have to pay when they get it for free."

"Get off my back with your morals, Emma."

"Get off *your* back, Ruby."

We sink into a dull and introverted silence. Emma's won, she's pulled us into a tangled self-consciousness, made us small in ourselves. I don't look at her for the rest of the night, turning my head away whenever she approaches, answering in grunts. She makes me afraid of what she can see in me, of letting her down. Emma once said she envied how I followed my urges, starting in my heart and moving outward. Not locked in my head like her, not buried in a heap of internal clutter.

She made me feel gigantic saying that. Now she's turned it inside out and made it an insult.

Thoughts don't swash in Emma's mind without form or gravity, the world isn't always new and rushing at her, understood in snippets, disjointedly, felt more than thought. These are the parts of me I don't want Emma to know and I close myself for protection.

I don't have an organizing philosophy, like Emma, to explain the things I do; I live in the full swell of instinct. I like being wanted, pulling myself up through other people's attentions, feeding myself on their worlds. I'm hungry like a starving person for passion, for intimacy, the warmth of ideas, revealed selves, joined briefly against this terror in the middle of me. I think it's my own ignorance, not knowing how to get out of my mind's confinement.

When learning comes it pulls like love and I race to it, acquiring through my fingertips, inside my belly, wanting to surrender to it. I don't want the damn football players, they're dull as a pail of rocks. It's Bill I crave. He brings me into the world, showing me new places, new tastes on my tongue: arugula, coriander, béarnaise, antipasto. I fill up my mouth and he watches, laughing at my reactions. Bill expects nothing; it exhilarates me and makes me want him more. There wasn't even any sex until last night, and it was fun and true. Making me feel safe and attached. Feeding my expanding self. Emma turns it into a robbery, makes me feel uncertain in my urges, makes me hide them secretly, shamefully. I am angry at Emma for that.

All night we circle each other, both of us demanding forgiveness the other cannot give. Equally stubborn. It's during this last intermission, when I'm taking my turn behind the snack bar, that Emma makes her final approach. The crowd has thinned out and we keep our voices low.

"Can we cut this crap?" Emma asks in her muscled-up tone. I walk away to the farthest end of the counter, near the office. Emma tries again, "You can do what you want."

"I don't need your permission," I tell her.

"I'm not giving it."

In that pause voices leak out of Johnny's office. Stupid, drunk ones. "Gorgeous man. Unfucking-believable." Panic passes between us. And a hurried, jumbled talk to spread over the men's noises. "Six or seven times. Man, I thought I was gonna have a heart attack."

My mouth sinks into my face. Emma touches my arm—"Fuck 'em," she whispers. "Just fuck 'em." I shake her off: "Shut up. I want to listen."

"She's a nice kid. And the body on her!" Then Johnny's voice. "She know you're getting married tomorrow?"

"You think I'd of got laid?"

It happens so fast neither one of us has time to form a plan or to stop one. We just react, Emma mostly, yanking herself into fierceness. Into her godawful shriek against Bill. She hurtles across the stairs and bashes open the office door.

"You sonofabitch," Emma howls, grabbing Bill by his shoulders and slamming him against the wall. She tells Johnny he's a puss-eating pimp. I stand back outside the door watching it all in slow motion. Johnny doesn't react at first, then a sneaky kind of pleasure spreads across his face. He yells something disgusting and starts pulling Emma off his friend, wedging his hands between shoulders, fingers, legs. Emma's coiled around Bill like a snake.

The yelling and shouting bring the strippers running, Ric too, and they stand, slack-jawed, at the door to the office. It's Abe, finally, who pins Johnny's arms to his sides. I stare numbly at Bill. He shrinks away from me, looking terrified and small. That's all I want to see.

Yvette says men are like bears, hibernating in the winter. The girls are moaning that the place is dead, but I don't care. I like the way the club curls into itself, how secrets swell and night smells wet and woolen. Even the bums tell better stories, hooking our hearts on pay night as they bunch around the door. Eden belongs to us again, to regulars like Marcel and the Old Man, to Vachek the shoeman.

Vachek sits by the rad hunched like a wizard, pulling at the wires of his beard. He comes almost every night now with his bags of shoes; he says we make his heart hot. I like the tinkle of his broken English, how it bubbles up bright as Christmas. "Only this club and Montreal I love, but French is no good for me." Vachek thinks Canada is dull as slush, grey as the civil servants who run this town. We're medicine, he tells us again, a vaccine against boredom. "Vachek the mad Czech," Emma used to call him. He misses her too. I wish she'd come back.

Johnny banned her for a month, but Emma stays away three just to spite him, dancing at the smudgy old BodyWorks with that teeny little stage you have to scrunch down on. All the girls hate it. I'd never dance there. But Emma won't forgive Johnny. Bill either. We got him good.

For a month we called up Bill's, ordering pizza deliveries to places that didn't exist, slit his car tires, made complaints to the health department, phoned in false fire alarms. I got bored. Not Emma. Last night she scrawled "Adulterer" on the front of Bill's house— Fat-Ass Gladys asks if I know about it. Vachek thinks it's all wonderful and claps his hands. He says Emma's got the guts of an artist.

Vachek was so many things in Czechoslovakia before the Russian tanks rolled in: an artist, engineer, teacher, film distributor. Now he works at National Defence buying supplies for the army, wheeling and dealing, which I guess is how he got into the business of organizing strip shows for the soldiers. "Democracy is licence to print money," he shrugs. "Be good citizen, make lots."

Vachek is always after us to do a show at the base—two hundred dollars, minus a commission for him and the club. I always say no because the other

girls say no and because Abe disapproves. Now Abe's
in Florida and tonight Ruby says she wants to try it.
She asks me to go too. Easy money, Vachek says.

Vachek never told us we'd have to sneak on to the
base pretending to be government clerks. He flashes
his I.D. card at the front gate, then drives us to the
mess. The inside is shiny and waxed like a school and
soldiers march us down the halls as if they're taking us
to the principal's office. Guard detail, they grunt.
When we pass the mess hall a crowd of guys starts
screaming and whistling. They feel big to me, muscley
like Dobermans. And there's no stage or lights, just a
bare patch of floor at the front. I tighten inside trying
to calculate my moves. We go to change in the ladies
room.

There's another girl with us, raggedy, with the bad
front teeth of a BodyWorks girl or maybe a whore
from Dalhousie Street. Buzzing on dexies, I think.
Nathalie's done this tons of times, she says, nothing to
it. But she's scared, I can tell. She won't look me in the
eye, won't even look at herself jabbing on makeup.
She's in a hurry, just wants to get out there and do it.
Ruby goes first with her bathtub act. It's a tough
crowd.

Ruby's music comes out thin and tinny on the
portable tape recorder. That's bad, I think, harder to
drown out the noise of the audience. The soldiers
shout over the music, lewd things. They're mean as
frat crowds that come into Eden, wanting to fight us

girls, to control us. I hate that shit. I don't know why
they do it. Yes, I do—to be important, to show off that
they can boss us around. But we just pull in like tur-
tles and move to the friendlier men.

Ruby gets hold of them finally by concentrating
fiercely on herself. The men quiet down and start leaning forward. At the end, the room thunders with
stomping feet. Ruby is glad it's over and shoots me a
cautioning look. I go on with my Riding Hood show
but I don't wander into the crowd as I do at Eden. I
know I have to hook them in fast and I dance like a
maniac, like I'm on fire. The music's so low they don't
know when the songs end or where to clap. I dance
right through the silences.

There's no protective space between us, no border.
The men reach out for me, grabbing my leg; one hurls
himself at my feet. I have to be funny about pulling
them off or they'll turn on me. I kick them comically
in the seat of their pants, but I kick them hard. I'm
winning them over until the end. They start squawking when I don't take my clothes off fast enough, when
I don't do spreads. I don't care, I'm hurrying away.

Nathalie comes out next, small and skittish. She
can't make herself bigger and I get mad watching her.
I don't know why. The men are mad too. They get
mean and frothy at the mouth, yelling ugly words:
"C'mon bitch," "Show yer tits." Nathalie's got no
protection, no ability or beauty to stop them, to barricade herself behind. I look at Vachek, wanting him

to do something. He just pulls on his beard and watches.

Nathalie is curling into herself, hunching her shoulders, covering her chest. The men keep taunting her, driving her into herself until she almost vanishes. Then suddenly she wobbles up straight, yanks off her bra, dives into the crowd, shaking her body in their faces. The room erupts in cheering. Nathalie's stumbling through the crowd getting pawed and grabbed at, bobbing like a cork among the men. Some guy grabs her G-string and sticks it in his mouth. Finally she limps back, but the men keep pulling at her. They're coming right on the dance floor now; a stubby drunk's got her arms pinned. Another one's holding her legs. "Oh Christ," Ruby blurts. This is bad, really bad. My neck tingles as if a spider's crawling on it.

Nathalie's hardly fighting now, just a set of terrified eyes. The two guys are swinging her like a sack, getting up the momentum to throw her into the crowd. More guys come, more hands, erasing the girl from view. "Do something, *fuck,* do something, Vachek," I'm screaming. He's white like a sheet and stiffened up. "Do something!" I push him hard and he staggers into the crowd. Ruby shouts that we've got to get out of there. Some of the men are eyeing us, moving toward us. I can see Vachek coming out of the crowd, pulling the naked girl free.

Ruby and I grab Nathalie and drag her down the hall. She's bony and hard as a fist. "Why'd you let them touch you?" Ruby yells at her. "You *never* let 'em touch you." The girl is mumbling incoherently, a jumble of hurt. "What are you saying?" Ruby shouts at her. "What?"

"...disappearing, disappearing..."

Nathalie looks up with hollowed eyes and I think of the drowned girl in the police photograph. How do they get that way? It's something about being poor and washed out by bad luck. It's something about stripping too.

I let the thoughts slide to the shadows inside me.

The Miss Nude Canada Pageant strikes with the force of lightening, spilling sparks through Eden and changing the course of hope. We swell in our imaginings, wanting to be lifted into stardom. Only Ruby holds back. Come on, I coax her, maybe she can win and get the trophy. Yvette thinks the worst it can be is another publicity stunt. Like the matinees, Emma guffaws, or the amateur hours or senior nights—man, were they deadly, we snicker.

Ruby moves away from the pageant instinctively, away from its whir and momentum. She says she feels its danger as cold as breath on her neck. Ruby can be weird sometimes. Ever since that night Vachek promised easy money, Ruby's been different. She says there's nothing easy about being erased. It's not just the show at the army base; it's the whole business— we're being crushed by hype and glitter, she thinks.

We're all disappearing. It sounds pretty doomsday, kind of Catholic. But then Ruby is. Or was.

I don't know much about Ruby's past, she's left it behind, unexamined, not like the rest of us, dragging in our old scabs and picking at them. Ruby's not reflective that way, she lives in the immediate world, in primary colours. What I know is accidental. She said once she'd grown up in a crowd of seven younger, squalling siblings; invisible, I think. She'd come up poor in Irishtown, hurrying to her chores, and into the squirming mysteries of early morning mass. In holy postponement, as she called it.

I've seen St. Patrick's Church, its big, squat knuckles on Nepean Street pressing down on that community. I can imagine Ruby sneaking out of it, claiming her own mysteries fiercely, her own subversive senses. Escaping into their hum. She grew visible to herself and then in the steamy haloes of boys. It's that escape, that searing shamelessness she reenacts every night. Her show. Her self.

Ruby loves plunging into herself on stage, loves the men's eyes bugging and their thoughts caving in, escaping together like renegades, in a conspiracy of urges. She invites them in expertly, beat by beat, row by row, growing immense in the warm flush of attention. It isn't that flabby, bullying kind of watching that had wounded Nathalie at the base or the dressed up kind that turns them all into actors. What Ruby gives is as sacred as the women she's heard about in the

Greek temples who danced and slept with the men who came to worship.

Some men won't look, or crease their faces disgustedly. Some think she's a whore. Ruby knows which ones they are: the guys in plaid shirts buttoned up to the top, golfers in cardigans, old guys, civil servants who wear their suits at night. They need to accessorize their urges with art or beauty, to protect their civilized selves from deeper instincts. Like those British colonists who dragged their fine china through Africa. Artifice is the enemy, Ruby knows, a returning to shame. So is hype.

Johnny's plan to stage the pageant in a nudist colony thirty miles out of town has nothing to do with the essentials of stripping. Ruby says we'll probably all look like hell in daylight. Especially Yvette, she means. Still, the rest of us hurry into our preparations, twitching over plans and escape routes to fame. Sugar wants to win so badly she has her toe hair removed by electrolysis. Emma and I joke about being interviewed on *The Late Show*.

Emma: "I'm really a nude poet, Mr. Carson...."

Me: "I'd like to donate my body to science...."

It isn't only being crowned Miss Nude Canada that thrills us. Johnny has promised a panel of celebrity judges. There'll be Playboy Bunnies, football stars, TV reporters and, best of all, an American agent. The hope that dangles in front of us, the secret, unsaid one, is being discovered and taken to Hollywood. The only obstacle is that none of us comes from other parts of Canada. Johnny tells us to pretend, so we heap on another layer of names. Emma becomes Miss Regina, Sugar, Miss Ottawa, I'm Miss Nude Toronto and Ruby, because of her ample chest, is Miss Vancouver. There's no title for Yvette and we manoeuvre gingerly around that silence. Nobody talks about Yvette, nobody can until Johnny says something. It takes him two months.

Yvette refuses to budge from her chair when Johnny comes into the dressing room. She says if he has something to tell her, he can tell her there. Then she leans into the mirror and applies her eyeliner. Ruby watches her admiringly. "You gotta understand our position here," Johnny squirms. Yvette keeps her eyes fastened on herself in the mirror, ignoring him. "Dammit, Yvette, you're too old for this."

Johnny wants to run after that but Yvette turns and pins him with her stare. "Is that so?" she says. "Den I 'ave no option but to resign." The room crumples. No, we blubber, don't. Yvette holds herself aloof from the pleading. She'd been thinking of leaving anyway, she tells us; girls get stale and places do too, she says. Nobody has the heart to argue with her.

"Dat's it and dat's all," she says firmly, pulling her gowns off the hangers. She's known this day was coming but I see her heart cramping, her eyes going blurry. Ruby sees it too. Perhaps Yvette feels the sting of time passing and a hot, sharp grief for Etienne.

Ruby watches her timidly, wanting to say some-thing, I think. Yvette has always blamed Ruby for bringing changes to the club and infecting the place with her spreads. Perhaps she blames her for this final shove out of here. But Yvette says it isn't Ruby's fault, it isn't the fault of any of us. It's the times, Yvette tells her, the aching detachment and unfeedable appetite. There's a frenzy out there to examine and touch every-thing, yet not to see or feel anything. To affect but not be affected. To go no deeper than sensation. Men have changed; they've become afraid of age, afraid of living, she says.

Ruby smiles as if she's been forgiven, Yvette too; each of them recognizing the other in this small moment. Refusing invisibility. Ruby says she will miss her.

Marcel hands me the lucky charm and smiles so sweet-ly I have to smile back. But I'm forcing myself, fishing it out of the angry swirling inside me. It's raining today, cold rain that falls sideways and fills up the holes in this stupid field. Yvette's revenge, I figure, and that feels soothing.

We're marching around in circles, in rows, like majorettes drilling, wearing only gold and red sashes across our torsos. I try to walk nicely for the judges, to not splash mud on the others. God, I hate Johnny. How could he do that to Yvette? I hate Eden and now I hate this pageant. We're in a cow pasture, for chris-sakes. I thought a nudist colony was like a golf club, but no, there are just fields here and a few wooden cabins dolled up with balloons and ribbon. And a covered little platform for the judges. I'm going to talk to that agent after this round of judging. I'm going to get the hell out.

There are loads of news people at the contest, pointing cameras, wanting us to pose, to stop our shivering. What are they going to do with those pictures? It hurts piling up smiles; the muscles in my cheeks are knotted like rope. Now there's some Montreal chick rolling up in a pink Corvette, movie star sunglasses perched on her head, long hair down to her waist, hiding a long, saggy chest. But who cares—the overall effect is blinding. Damn that Johnny, he said this contest was for local girls.

The rain falls down in bucketsful and still Johnny is screaming at us from under his umbrella. "Come on, girls, look sexy, you can do it. The boys want a good show." The "boys" herd around us like buffalo, fat and shaggy and wet. Twelve hundred of them paid fifty dollars a head. Poor Emma, the rain bothers her allergies. She's red and swollen again.

"Hey, girls, can ya all squeeze in together?"

"Miss, can you put your arms behind your head?"

"Whadya say yer name was, sweetheart?"

I've got to get to that American agent, Peter Rabitt. What kind of weird name is that anyway? I've got to get him to book me somewhere.

Boy, did I want to win this contest. Maybe I still do. The wanting's gone all soggy, though, and belongs to someone else. I thought of not coming, of standing up to Johnny and saying I quit, like Yvette. For Yvette. How could he do that to her? She was old but he did-n't have to say it so fast and hard. And her leaving in the cab, not wanting me to help her with her stuff, just disappearing down the stairs, fading away from me. Damn him.

Maybe Ruby's right about Eden getting too phony and fake. But hype is part of being professional. Ever since Rae Darren I've wanted to build myself up into something bigger; not pumped full of plastic or my hair ballooned out like Priscilla Presley. I want the shows, the gadgets, the big and easy confidence. I want to swallow fire and design my own costumes. I'm good at dreaming up ideas and themes, fitting them together—I like the artistic part. I've been afraid of leaving Eden, scared of getting squashed out there. I'm not anymore.

I spot Peter Rabitt hunched over the hotdog stand, a hefty guy with a puffy grey beard. I rush up, telling him how great he is, how much I've heard about him. Is he taking on any new acts, I ask, is he interested? Whoa, he says. My words are pouring over him too fast; I stop and put spaces between them.

Sugar is watching me from across the field, puck-ering her face as if she had eaten something sour. She's been sucking up to the crowds and posing for pictures, wanting so bad to win. She probably thinks I'm but-tering up the judge.

Peter Rabitt says he'd like to see my show and do I have pictures? I don't tell him about the embarrassing shots of me posing in a field with a bathing suit. Not good ones, I lie, but I'm planning to get some. Don't, he says, he's got a photographer in Chicago. Chicago? He says we should talk later. Definitely, I say, repeating the word so I can shape it right. Definitely. DEFinitely. DefinITELY. Like I'm a fucking moron.

Holy shit, I think, I've got to tell Emma. Emma's hiding in the cabin and drinking Sugar's gin when I tell her about the agent. She doesn't snarl as I expect. She says I'm smart to get out. "You're all right, kiddo."

Thanks, I say, wincing at that name.

"I gotta idea," I tell her, pointing to the wall behind her. I grab a marker and scrawl huge words, a poem for Johnny. She busts out laughing. I love Emma. If I do leave I'll miss her red, wet face and her constantly sniffing nose.

It's still raining when we saunter back outside for the judges' announcement. The place is deserted. The men have gone with their photographs, leaving behind bottles and film boxes. We pick our way through the mud and litter, reciting my poem:

> "May the fiery crud beset him
> And burn away his feet
> And may crabs as big as nutmegs
> Get on his balls and eat
> And when he's old and lonely

And a syphilitic wreck
May his head fall through his asshole
And break his fucking neck."

CHAPTER 6

"Canada's Top Young Show Exotic"

Fonda,

You probably think this is childish but I wanted to ask you something before you would go south for three months. Though it's kind of stupid, would you mind if you could write to me if you would get a chance. I'm one of your fans!

So anyways, have a good time and as you would say: "Take it easy—but take it!" I'll miss you.

Yours, Sandy

America rushes past me in the window, exciting me like a drug, jangling my nerves. Chicago is immense, all grey and smokestacked at its edges. I've lived only forty miles from the American border, but I've never been to the States before. I want to scream "Hello, America" and "Greetings from Canada." I want them to know I came in second in the Miss Nude Canada pageant—the Montreal girl came in first and just thinking of Sugar's screwed-up face makes me chuckle. Being second doesn't sound as good as first runner-up like it says in my contract. I tug the yellow paper from the envelope again, reading the letterhead and my stage name on it: "Les Stars, Artist Management, Riviera Beach, Florida."

I like how the letters wiggle across the page like little dancing boots. Artistic. And the stern weight of all the whereases and therebys. Especially the last paragraph: "This contract is play or pay, other than an Act of God." I don't know what it means but it sure as hell sounds serious.

I find the studio on Jackson Boulevard and race up the stairs, two at a time. Ricardo the photographer is an old man, Italian, I think, bowed like a crab and peering up at me. He asks if I ever pluck my eyebrows. I pull my face back defensively. Never mind, he says, I might have my own natural beauty. It's a compliment I cling to as he leads me to the back.

The changing room is a shrine, plastered with girls' photographs, autographed in big bold curlicues and lip prints. Ricardo lingers on the pictures, examining his work, whispering the women's names, possessing them. The strippers have huge hair and big pouty mouths that swell up like welts on their faces, and little hands, and feet like talons. And skinny, snaky eyebrows. They look fake and odourless like fifties starlets, I think. I study how their bodies twist; heads turned one way, chests another, tilted forward like carts unloading apples. Saying "Come," saying "Don't," all mixed up and spinning. I try deciphering these elements of glamour.

Ricardo says there are really only two types of girls: she-devils and dollies. Which one am I? I don't know, how can you think of a thing like that? The she-devils remind me of B-movie vampires the way they force their stares so fiercely. The girlie-girls are soft and doughy with eyes that drift away from their bodies, wounded as the sweater girls from school. Maybe I'm something in between, I say. Maybe I'm not them at all.

My hands flutter nervously when Ricardo aims his camera. He tells me to curve my back like the girls in the photographs, to bend forward. I feel so phony. I want to act out my show, to stoke my heat. I leap into my dancing, fluttering my costumes, snapping my limbs at the camera. The camera snaps back, like teeth, I think. Ricardo shouts at me to slow down, to freeze into poses. I can't. The big stars do it, Ricardo says, and it makes me mad. Back and forth, cat and mouse, we go all morning: me trying to reveal my internal self, Ricardo slapping me back into sexpot poses.

When I finally agree to model in my panties and bra with my trophy, Ricardo says I have too much hair at my bikini line. Maybe I want to fix it. I don't. I'm not one of those smooth-shaven she-devils or whatchamacallits. So what? Isn't this my five hundred dollars? Can't I decide how I'll look?

I'm biting back my fury when I feel something sticky on my thigh. Something warm. Oh no, not now, not here. I press my legs together, contracting every muscle in a single squeezing act of concealment. I don't want Ricardo knowing; oh Jesus, I'm going to die of embarrassment. I fumble off the platform and hurry to the bathroom.

I wash the blood from the fabric, watching how it curls in the water like smoke. The blood undulates in the ripples, then goes spiralling down the drain. When the water runs clear and the sink is white again, I pluck my hair and go back to Ricardo.

Calumet City isn't the gangster town I was expecting. It's a pulled-in place, humming with neon beer signs. Only the liquor stores and gun shops are lit up and watchful, and the blinking, broken marquee at Joey's.

Joey's hangs loosely to the side of the Franklin Hotel. It's smoky inside and cramped with old men and working guys talking mournfully about Squeaky Fromme's bullet missing President Ford. Joe the owner wears a long, white butcher's apron and asks me do I

know how to mix? Sure, I tell him, thinking he means
with the other girls. He curls his face skeptically. I'm
going to have to watch out for Joe.

The girls are soft and flabby, not muscular or pink-
skinned like the ones at Eden. They're old like Yvette,
but blonder, at the end of something. They want to
know about Canadian clubs and act surprised when I
tell them we don't sell booze. How do I make money?
they ask. They don't care for dancing as much as talking with the men. They shuffle on the stage, looking
as if they'll float away. They don't go nude, either, just
to their G-strings and the tassely things stuck to their
nipples. It's the law, one of them tells me, they gotta
wear pasties. I don't have any so they make me wear
Band-Aids instead.

The club feels closed as a family, turned in on its
own habits and faces. It's a bar, not a theatre like Eden.
The men are at tables, bunching noisily around the
girls. They hardly lift their eyes to the show. But my
first night is good, I get the guys watching and even
applauding a little. Everyone asks me to sit at their
table and wants to know my real name. I lie and say
it's Miki. I don't like getting so close to the customers,
it chews up my nerve.

The man in the back is different. He's been watching me intensely, smiling when our eyes catch. He says
his name is Merrill and could he buy me a drink? I
order ginger ale and Joey brings champagne. The cost
embarrasses me but Merrill doesn't mind. He's beautiful. I like the way he listens, how his eyes stay on my

face. When he has to leave the club feels emptier. So do I. I wander out to the lobby.

"You from out of town, sweetie?" the little voice asks from the corner. Alberta doesn't have a neck, just a lumpy sack of a body slumped beside the pay phone. She says she's waiting for her son to call. "You like crochet, honey?" Alberta fumbles beneath her sweaters for her dolls and doilies to show me.

She lives in the hotel, in a room with a sink and TV. And two hot meals a day, she says, as if it's something to be proud of. I can't tell her age from her apple-doll face; maybe she's forty, maybe she's eighty. Alberta roams in her mind for bits of her past to bait me with, to keep me talking. She asks if I'm a showgirl; I feel shy admitting it to an old lady like her. "It's honest work, sweetie, honest work." She lingers on the work part. When I tell her I have to go, Alberta heaves herself up and pulls open a huge orange afghan for me to admire. "You wanna buy a raffle ticket?" Alberta says she knits things to raffle in the club. She does it for the young people who like to gamble, and for the money to feed her cats. I buy four chances.

By the second night at Joey's I get what's going on, but only because Joe hollers it to me. The dancing part is just decoration; what Joe wants is for the customers to buy the girls drinks. Mixing, he calls it. The strippers make a commission: six dollars on every bottle, one dollar on every drink. I make eight dollars on Tuesday sitting with Merrill and three on Wednesday. By Thursday Joe's barely talking to me.

I'm bad at faking that giggly talk or jiggling the men on a line like the other girls do. Merrill says I tell too much about myself: my favourite poet, Dylan Thomas, my feelings for the poor, life after death. The men seem surprised and squirm away from me, ashamed of something. I try to listen, to hear them, but they go faint sometimes like a radio signal, crackling with whispered confessions I can't understand. Some soften slowly and I have to peel their toughness carefully. I don't want them paying for me, though. I know what Yvette would think; I can see her shaking her head.

In a funny way, Alberta reminds me of home. I sneak out to her whenever Joe's not looking. Sometimes he chases after me and I'm hauled back. One time I go to Alberta's room and it surprises me that a whole life can be shrunk into such a small place. Her room smells like a fish market and it's stuffed with dolls and cats and tins of Miss Mew. And lots of unopened mail. Alberta can't read. I've never met an adult who can't read. She says it's a pity but she doesn't need to now that the social security people send her cheques directly to the hotel. Joe gives her whatever's left from her room and board. It's never enough to buy cat food.

She always wants to hear about the glamorous places I've been. Let's go touring, she'll say, and I make up things to tell her. Sometimes I borrow Yvette's stories, sometimes we go to my dream places: Ireland, France, Tibet. Tonight when I tell her about Canada,

Alberta is amazed that doctors are free. She says she likes Canadians because Guy Lombardo plays "Auld Lang Syne" every New Year. But she thinks the president of Canada is a communist for liking Castro. Prime Minister Trudeau isn't bad, I tell her. In Cuba even prostitutes are taught to read, which is more than her government ever did for her. Alberta's mulling it over with the full force of herself when Joe comes looking for me. He barks at Alberta to stop interfering with business and to get the hell back to her room. "Sorry, Joe, sorry. I'm just a crazy old bat," she says wobbling to her feet. Alberta folds in her mind and disappears.

After that I don't care too much about pleasing Joe.

The next night he calls me over to the bar, dangling the phone like a noose. He says my agent wants to talk to me. Peter Rabitt tells me the club's not renewing my contract for the second week. My throat tightens. Joe's grinning at me and I force myself to grin back. "Great," I say. I think Rabitt's going to be mad at me but he says he's proud I lasted the week. Joey's is a real tough place.

"I won't miss it," I tell him loudly so Joe can hear. Joe waits for me to finish. Do I want to know why he doesn't hire Canadian girls, he asks. Not really. "Because they're candy-asses," he sneers.

After that the girls at Joey's are nicer to me, in a way I imagine people are to the dying. Now that I'm almost gone they tell me secrets about Joey's, how it's run as a welfare hotel for the mob. I don't know if it's true but I like imagining Joe in a shoot-out, lying in a pool of blood. So does Merrill, who says a girl like me doesn't need Joey's. It sounds like a line from a Bogart film. I know he means it. He says he'll find me in my tour.

On my last night the girls and I pull Alberta into the club for the raffle draw. She is beaming as we call the customers to attention. She's raised one hundred and twenty dollars, a club record. One of the old guys pulls out the ticket. It's mine. I win the afghan and Alberta hugs me tight.

"I'm glad it's you," she says. I am too.

Dear Sweetie,

I write this letter feeling the need to have you near. I can't find an explanation for my ever-present thoughts of you. I don't mean to imply love because I've never been lucky enough to share that with anyone.

Engineers are suppose to deal in logic and facts, but with you it's emotions and dreams. Please write or call soon.

Merrill

The Red Dot in Grand Rapids, Michigan, is starchy with its business suits and middle-aged couples. I like to escape to Smitty's Pancake House across the street. It's open twenty-four hours and I love the blueberry crepes. Howard the widower looks for me there. He's always trying to be helpful, fixing my trunk when it breaks, buying me takeout.

Merrill comes for a visit and I am surprised how my breath catches. I watch his loose and lanky walk, how he slides into his seat, cradling his chin in his long fingers. Lost and found at the same time, man and boy. Men fall harder in love in the States, I discover; they follow me from city to city, worshipful. They want to show me something precious of themselves: an old army photograph or a poem. Sometimes I feel disloyal, as if I'm cheating on them. They don't want sex—though I wish they would so I could feel older. They want to talk to me or take care of me, like Howard. He keeps leaving sightseeing information and notes for me at the bar. I feel sorry for him and I promise to write back.

> *Dearest,*
> I will always remember you. Stay as fresh as you are. I will never, never forget you. See you in Pittsburgh.
> *Howard*

Howard looks like a cop in the crowded club in Pittsburgh. He comes twice with flowers for me, then retreats to Michigan. I am relieved.

Riders is a biker bar, like a zoo with its bulky, tattooed creatures hurtling through the air, over chairs and tables and across the stage. In between, the strippers dance furiously to the thud of Bachman Turner

Overdrive and Steppenwolf. They are blonde and acrobatic, gyrating on the stage and along the bar, bending down for the bills the bikers stuff in their G-strings. Focussed. Cold. Americans love blondes.

"Fuck Barry Manilow music," the sign by the cash says.

The bikers look mean, dressed all in black, clogging the door, but they don't mix much or need affection. They come for the dancing and music, shaking their hair like wet dogs, howling when they like a song or a dance.

I feel strong among them. I dance hard and sweaty to Janis Joplin, building up my momentum. God, I love dancing, the pure physical hum of it. I don't linger in poses or interrupt my body's instincts. I charge into the sharp sting of existence, into primitiveness. There are so many things I've learned about stripping, but dancing is the core of it. The returning to ancient selves.

I am held over for three weeks in Pittsburgh. Later, when I think of my American tour, it is the bikers I remember best—their black leather and hard voices circling my primitive self.

Hey, Chick,
Take a piece of my heart. You're amazing. So is Janis. Right on!
    A fan, Studebaker

Indianapolis surprises me. Ricardo's pictures have arrived and are fanned out in the front windows. They're good, I think, not phony like those other ones. My face still looks babyish and not even my hardest look changes that. At the bottom are the words "Canada's Top Young Show Exotic."

I like the crazy mood of the Zodiac club and the owner, Bernie, who indulges us girls like a father. I like the go-go dancers who serve beer and fling themselves on stage for three quick songs. They're young as me, college girls or divorced mothers, on their way to somewhere else, not dented like the girls at Joey's. They don't even strip, just dance around in bathing suits.

It's a college crowd and we are wild as children, playing tag with each other, staging pajama parties and watergun fights, forcing all the normal rules to bend to us. We snicker at the old men, then finish our shifts and escape. I rush into the night with the Zodiac girls, to the after-hours clubs. Picking up men and playing excessively.

The clubs are blurring and I'm missing home and the girls at Eden. I lean toward Nashville with the last of my hope, wanting its fame, hoping for Merrill. He's promised in his letters to meet me there.

The Pink Lizard Lounge smells of cigars, like an old bordello. It's padded in velvet and shadows. Grandly faded. The men are arranged by importance: the rich ones in the back booths, the poorer men and black ones at the front. The owner likes me at first, taking me in with one deep breath, feeling into my character. Coming into a club is like being adopted; they can say yes or no on first look. So I push my whole character up into my face, my spunk and good intentions. Sometimes I blur my intelligent part so they don't get afraid that I might unionize or something. For the Lizard I push up my gentler, vaguer side to match the place.

Randall says he runs a gentleman's club and he doesn't want his strippers hustling drinks or looking cheap. He wants us to do our show, then mingle with the customers as ladies. I like the challenge. I sit with the men in the front seats and back, imagining myself as Scarlett O'Hara, throwing back my head and covering my mouth when I laugh. I'm getting good at waiting for questions, at talking slow and quiet. When Merrill comes I sit with him in the fatter back booths and we sink together in whispers. Merrill doesn't monopolize my time without paying. He buys me champagne and the other strippers too. He tips well and the waitresses stay close and eager. Randall watches sourly. I see it but I can't feel into it, I can't reach my mind to its meaning, but there's something he doesn't like.

Whatever it is, the strippers forgive me at first. I'm a northerner, they say, as if the North is an ignorant place. They want to help me, telling me to concentrate on the big spenders, to keep clear of the riffraff. If I know what they mean. Halfway through the week I start feeling a strange withholding in the club and an inability to win the crowd to my side. Randall begins shooing me away from the customers as if I've done something wrong. Even the dressing room goes mute, sucking in its chatter when I come in the room. I wish I could pull back the skin of their secrets.

I'm so relieved when Merrill comes late and takes me from the Lizard. He won't sit in the club anymore and he doesn't say why. I guess it's his possessiveness. He stays with me at night and I feel soothed under his damp, dark skin. I'm different from American girls, he tells me, as if he can't believe it himself. We touch strong and deep inside each other, clear in our loving. Ferocious. I don't feel bad about sleeping with Merrill. It sounds bald all by itself: sleeping with customers. People expect it when they hear I'm a stripper. That's why I've kept clear of it since Bill.

On Thursday, the strippers start chanting in a circle on the floor, mumbling words that make me lean in closer. Emmaline says they are part of an old Southern tradition, songs they sing back in the woods. Have I ever heard of the Klan, they ask. Clan? Is it the name of a club? I answer. "Yeah, sort of," they snicker derisively. I turn away from their cat talk, folding back into myself.

I come in tonight with my usual hellos but the strippers turn their backs. One by one they close on me. On purpose. I pretend not to care and pull my spine straight as I saunter to the back. The dressing room is empty when I stumble in. I'm cold in my guts and shaking. Thinking of ways to wound them. Then something sharp grabs my eye—big, black scrawls all over the mirror and on my bags too: "Nigger Lover." "White Trash." The words make no sense, they're not from my language, but I understand the scratchiness, the hard, mean lines. The letters splay at the end, sharp and ragged as barbed wire. Like those keep out signs on broken-down fences.

The goddamned dirty bitches. It's Merrill they're after because Merrill is black. I stare through the strippers as I pass them looking for Randall. I want him to know, to do something. I think he is listening until he drags out his drawl. He says he's heard I'm a disruptive influence from the other girls. The world tilts. "Consideration of others is the hallmark of civility," he says. "And critical for labour relations in a fine club such as this. That you lack these attributes might suggest you seek an engagement elsewhere." Me? It's the other girls who've scribbled all over my bag, I stutter. It's them.

"We don't want your kind. You're fired." Fired? My kind? What was my kind? My thoughts can't get to my tongue fast enough and glue together in the heat of my rage. What the hell is my kind in their Nazi, hate-mongering minds? But all I can do is sneer.

Randall watches me indifferently and I feel stung by a sudden invisibleness. It's the same thing they've done to Merrill, erasing both of us with their slippery talk, making us cheap.

I want to stand up to them. I know my contract lets me. I'm stuck in my hate, though, in my shabby, vicious words. I can't let them out, I can't let Randall and those girls feel superior. I demand my money and Randall pays me my wages in one-dollar bills.

I tell Merrill, trying to make it sound funny. He flinches at the hurt I bring him, in the world I've let slip in. In his ugly America. How many times have I heard these men talk about their rights, about their great country? How much excitement did I bring here, thinking it was the centre of something?

I'm ashamed of what I've seen and my shame becomes Merrill's. Or always was. It's a terrible silence growing between us, forcing us onto either side of this wound. It's the last thing we share before he fades away from me.

I want to go home now. I feel it like an ache. I want to go back to Canada.

CHAPTER 7

La Grande Vedette

Rabitt tells me not to give up on touring, to go with my momentum. I wanted to be a star, streaking through America, looking down on Eden from far off. Gigantic. But I feel defeated by Nashville and its sticky hatred, by my own thin-skinnedness. I can't ignore the meanness of the clubs, or how it dents the Merrills and Albertas. I keep getting slapped off my course by the human parts of stripping. Maybe I'm *not* professional enough, maybe I never will be. Rabitt is right, I can't go back to Eden. It's the summer of the Olympics and

I feel the pull of Montreal like a second chance. Rabitt says the SexOHrama is the biggest strip club in Montreal, the best.

The owner has a long, sharp ferret face and I'm cautious at first. Jean-Claude's eyes move over me, lingering on my feet and legs mostly. His office is paneled, crammed with girlie calendars and garters and stockings. J.C. asks if I wear stockings in my show. I know the answer he wants.

There is something wounded about J.C., something sensitive about his pointed overbite and concave chest, his arms dangling like string. He speaks softly to the girls who keep interrupting—offering advice, handing out tampons from the top drawer of the filing cabinet, polite. I trust him. When he asks me to sleep with him finally, at the end of the meeting, it's with an aching formality. I decline and he shrugs apologetically. He had to try. I know.

I am hovering in the foreignness of J.C.'s club, prickling at the beginning of myself again, when I hear a string of words, stinging ones that bring a gush of homesickness. I hurry through the dark. "Emma Goldman," I yell at the edge of the stage. She turns and jumps right into my arms. The men laugh with us and applaud. "What the hell are you doing here?"

"Johnny is an asshole. This place is amazing. They love me, man. Now fuck off, my fans await." Emma slides off me and the club becomes safe as home.

I move in with Emma right away, at Residence Anick, where all the strippers stay. We laugh and drink

and sleep every day until noon. It's scary how easy it is
to disappear in the clubs, how exhausted and vague I
can get. Sometimes in the States I would stay in bed
all day instead of nosing into places I'd never see again.
Sometimes staying curious requires such force.

Montreal yanks me into daylight, into bigger life,
shaking me loose from darker margins. Every street
corner is claimed by artists, dancers, musicians,
speaking in the language of my mother and aunts, in
a French I begin to remember. Emma and I go like
spies to the alternative galleries, to Vehicule, sniffing
at the old poets' readings, the fading generation of
philosopher professors in their grey beards and sports
coats. We're relieved that what we do on stage is more
interesting. We are artists, not simply strippers;
Montreal assures us of that and we assure each other.
Even J.C. allows our artistic indulgences, forgiving us
when we're late, or when we want a night off to attend
a poetry reading.

Sunday afternoons we spend in book stores,
Emma buying Noam Chomsky, Saul Alinsky and
something called *Sisterhood Is Powerful*. I discover the
Imagists and grab every ragged book by Pound and
H.D. and William Carlos Williams, promising myself
that I will write more. I find Isadora Duncan, too, and
adopt her as my barefoot muse. At night we head to
Ben's for cheesecake, or the Moustache for a last blast
of disco. There's ouzo at La Scala or jazz at La Nuit
Magique in Vieille Montreal, where I linger for a
hoped-for glimpse of Leonard Cohen, my hero. When

we feel bored we say we're strippers and men drop at our feet, doors open, drinks arrive, although sometimes our luck runs out and we get stuck with drunk American tourists. But we can always escape—we have lots of our own money.

Ruby shows up at the end of July, completing an old circle, bringing us news from home. Eden is getting dull, she says, everyone's heading to Montreal. What about Sugar, we want to know. "Still headlining, but Ric's left her. Living with a French chick, working another club."

"There is a God," I yelp. "Probably not," Emma quips, but we grin together viciously.

"Yvette's coming too."

"Yvette!"

"She's not dancing anymore, she's making costumes." My heart twists. Yvette always had such beautiful costumes, always took such pride in them. But to be reduced to making them for other girls, it's got to humiliate her, I think, and I feel a cold hate against Johnny. "No, it's okay, she wants to do it," Ruby assures me.

Ruby is pale and more hyper than usual, twitchy. She's working the Bar Maurice down in the east end, the Dubois place. I've heard rumours about the Dubois brothers selling guns and bad dope. Ruby says she's trying to get into the SexOHrama, but she's happy at the Bar Maurice. I want to believe her and promise to visit her, although I suspect it may take a long time. Montreal is so distracting, and the club.

There's a rounder, stronger femaleness in the SexOHrama than at Eden, and more laughter. Ten strippers work every day, mostly English, but American too, and thirty go-gos. The strippers change every week, working the city circuit—it's not the same Peyton Place as Eden, where we grew like thorns in each other's lives. The dressing room's a pigsty and the toilet never works but we manoeuvre around the broken parts, and around each other, speaking with our hands, in pieces of each other's language, instantly friends. I feel other currents, too, a whispering in French, resentful, I think, of the English girls. It's the murmur of ownership, and of displacement, the sounds I remember making in Eden when the Americans came.

The SexOHrama is a frontier, the Wild West, in the weeks of the Olympics. Delegations from all over the world pack into the place and hundreds of soldiers, loafing after their Olympic security work. The men's adoration is exquisite, the way I'd imagined from Yvette's old burlesque stories. The Japanese throw hundred-dollar bills at the blonde girls, the Italians wave their arms and pound their hearts dramatically. *"Bella, bella,"* they scream. The Germans just sit there getting drunk; so do the Russians, except they're louder before they pass out. The Chinese cluster around the hard, sweaty dancers like me. They're short and serious in their identical suits and horn-rimmed glasses—dwarf Mormons. Rings of them form by the office door, trying to negotiate with

J.C.—they think we're prostitutes. It always stings me, people thinking I'm a whore, believing the most obvious lies about me. Wanting to. I'm growing a thicker skin, though, learning to laugh at them.

There are darker layers in the club, a lurking, ferocious maleness trying to get control of us. I see it in the flinching of the go-go girls—how they detour around the agents and doorman, around the small man, Jean Valle, clinging to the corners of the club. Valle wears a black patch on one eye and I feel sorry for him. *"Ma belle, c'est une bonne show,"* he says, uncurling his grin at me. He's the biggest agent in the city and wants to sign me up: twenty percent from me and another twenty from the club. J.C. warns me off him. He doesn't like Jean Valle signing up girls at the SexOHrama. I know J.C. is a master at reading character.

I often sit at the back table, watching the show and making friends with the doormen. There are six of them, wearing their manners professionally, like funeral parlour attendants. They circle the customers, policing them with whispers or, when that fails, hoisting them out by their collars. The doormen prefer the big shows, the clean, old-style girls, or energetic ones like me. They hate the go-gos— *"Sont des maudites vaches"*— they're damned cows, Mario, the big one, mutters.

But I like the go-gos. They work hard slinging drinks, dodging hands, climbing on stage twenty times a night for a quickie strip down to their G-strings. Emma says they're worse than TV commercials— "interrupting the show. Fucking up concentration." I think she's jealous. The go-gos are better dancers than we are, more connected to the crowd. They're our allies, loosening the men and chatting them up, even risking arrest—girls in strip bars aren't allowed to talk to the customers, except for taking orders. It's an unnatural law, forcing the girls into chilly curtness, making them jumpy. J.C. says Mayor Drapeau brought it in for Expo 67 to stop the prostitutes from pestering tourists, but we're not hookers. The cops don't see the difference; they keep charging girls with soliciting. I've never seen so many cops all over the club, every single night. The uniformed ones aren't so bad—*"sur le bras"*—on the take, some cash and drinks, some flirting. I think they're cute in their handlebar mustaches and besides, they're not working vice. It's the plainclothes ones with their long, blank faces who hate us.

I plunge into the whirl of the Olympics crowds, experimenting with Isadora Duncan shapes, with new steps and pauses. There's so much blurring of bodies at the SexOHrama that nakedness becomes almost mundane and beauty gets ordinary. There's an odd sameness, a kind of vacuum. The men want something more, I think, they need to be surprised back into their humanness. I try reaching into the crowd, making them laugh, conspiring with them. It's a startling power: "Okay, it's a long show, hands up if you need to pee." Sometimes I cut off their ties, or make fun of their baldness—"Now here's a lover of gigantic proportions." I drag them on stage for my nurse show, tying them up and pretending to examine

them—"You're not scared being naked in a roomful
of strangers, are ya?" The men howl with laughter at
being made fools of, at watching each other. "Hey, sad
sack," I call to the shy first-timers in the back. "Are
you missing the mother-in-law?" The men enjoy
being part of the show; the old ones ringside crane for
attention—"Dad, is that you?" I cry, crushing them
with hugs. My mind and body work together, con-
necting into a stronger persona, flashing with lightening speed through the faces and needs in the place.
The businessmen scowl impatiently, wanting the
goods and not the gab. "You're not here to see me
naked, are ya?" I ask loudly. They try to ignore me at
first. "Men like you don't want to see my barenaked
breasts and my barenaked butt, do you?" Small smiles
inch over a few of them. "You're here for my superior
mind, right?" I even make the women laugh—"How's
about we go for a drink and leave these degenerates
behind?" I hurl my comments, not to push the audience away as Emma does, but to invite them into
contact, into intimacy; to share a common humanness.

The go-gos love me for rousing the crowds and
getting them drinking. Even Yvette, when she finally
drops by, says my show has improved. That makes me
soar. Still, she can't help admonishing me for going
barefoot and complains about my costumes. Now that
she's a costume-maker, she just wants my money, I
tease her.

"Absolutely. And you 'ave to pay me lots to make *you* look good."

I live the summer quickly, deeply, learning about poetry and performance, growing sturdier in myself. Yvette sews beautiful beaded bras and panties, making me shinier. When the Olympics finish, the club goes stiller and the city fades a little, becoming more internal, more French, belonging less to me. Another fever claims Montreal, the provincial election, and the fiery words of René Lévesque. All summer and fall separation rages through the veins of the city, pouring out of the televisions and radios and taxis, dividing friendships along ancient creases. I watch the go-gos dancing fiercely to "Gens de pays," and Gille Vigneualt's "Mon pays c'est l'hiver," stirring the crowds. Most of them are French and they embrace their sudden popularity, ascending above the strippers and the smallness of their fate.

On election night I book off sick to see Ruby's show. The whole city is in the streets, great loud swells of faces and fluttering blue and white flags. The separatists have won. My taxi can't get through and I have to walk, pushed along.

"J'me souviens"—I remember, the crowds scream. On the corner of rue Berri, a half-naked man painted blue shouts down at me from a lamp pole, *"Nous sommes libres, je t'aime tout le monde."* I carry his perfect hope all the way to Ruby's club.

When I tumble into Bar Maurice the outside world recedes. It's a biker club, but different from the one in Pittsburgh. These guys are stupid and mean, pawing at the girls. There's a heavy blanket of fear and bad feelings over the place. The girls are thin, with scooped out, jaundiced faces. Everybody's drunk or stoned, including Ruby. She's wobbly on stage, spilling out of herself, without the internal control I remember her having at Eden. She never used to play to the crowd—now she's flopping all over them drunkenly. Ruby says she can understand French better when she drinks; by that accounting, I tell her, she should be a professional translator by now. But it's not just booze, it's the drugs, she's glazing over, living in slow motion.

By the end of her third show, she's barely moving. At first I think she's just playing possum on the carpet, then I hear the snoring—she's passed out. The busboy tries blasting the music but she won't wake up. Then he turns off the spot and drags her from the stage. The men are yelling and laughing at her and I want to break their faces. "That's my friend up there. Shut the fuck up," I shout back. *"Vas chïer, maudite anglaise"*— fuck off, English, they snarl. It's all crazy and jumbled, and then the doorman yanks me by my arm and I'm trying to push free, trying to get to Ruby. "Let go of me," I'm yelling.

"J'elle connais, laissez faire"—let her go, I know her. It's Valle, wearing his greasy grin. *"Merci,"* I gasp as the creep lets go and I race toward the dressing room. Some tattooed bastard is shaking Ruby when I

get backstage, pouring water on her face, practically drowning her. I push him off. Ruby's limp as a doll and I haul her up roughly. "Come on, damn it, you're going home." My hands are shaking with anger. Ruby should be soaring in Montreal, claiming her talents, but instead she's fading away, just another loser chick, a druggie—and I don't know why. "Wake up," I bark. I'm frightened by this Ruby and her failure. I can remember her confidence in Eden, how the men adored her.

I drag Ruby back to the Anick and Emma rants furiously against the clubs and owners: "Let's set fire to Bar Maurice." I don't try to win against Emma's simple certainties. Ruby's wounds have to do with Ruby, I think, not the Dubois or any club. It's something about boundaries and containment, about authenticity. I don't want it to happen to me, to disappear or to grow all prickly the way Emma has, just to keep myself intact. I talk to JC and he grudgingly agrees to try Ruby for a week. He sees something in her he's seen before.

I am flushed in my party mood, mixing my laughter in with the other strippers', when I see Angele Duchamps. She reminds me of a fortuneteller tonight, scarves around her head and matching mumu. Angele is weathered brown like hide, fading from a brilliant beauty. The girls all need her, and fear her. No one knows how many years Angele's been trolling the clubs and galas, looking for stories and stars—*vedettes,* she calls them—for *Sextra* magazine, the girlie tabloid. "La Sexpert de *Sextra,* dey call me," she says, glistening in her drunkenness. The girls cluster around, making themselves interesting so she'll write down their stories. But Angele hardly scribbles anything in her notepad; instead, she's trying to get the girls to pose nude for her photographer. I turn back from her web, into the hum of the club.

Galas are just glorified club openings. The new club books ten or twenty strippers into a single night, hoping to pack in customers. Small galas are embarrassing but it's a big one tonight, a good one; I can feel it, lots of cops and girls. Nikkie the Vampire Girl is here with her new space show, Black Sheba from Chicago, too. Galaxy Starr, Lemmy Sea, Yannick London, Bonny Bubees, Renee Paris, Juana Ball, Nova-Jade, Lisa Storm, Connie Lingus and Emma too, with her stupid pig. I tell her it's a bad idea doing the pig show but Emma flicks her wrist dismissively: "Don't sweat it."

Emma's red and sore with her allergies tonight, cranky about doing a free show. So many clubs have opened all over the city and suburbs, I've done eight freebies in the last year. None of us gets paid to do a gala, just cab fare and a couple of cognacs, probably some food tonight, by the looks of it. I don't mind, I come for the fun.

Galas are our version of a Hollywood premiere: we pretend to be stars, mug for the press, catch up on gossip, appraise each other's costumes. And we try to persuade the owners to hire us. The agents come, too, scavengers, the same old bunch crowding in the back, posing with their dancers, sweet-talking the owner into an exclusive deal. Montreal agents are bullies, not like Rabitt. They muscle the girls to work bad clubs, to do free shows, conning them into dependency. They have their tentacles in every part of the business: costumes, photos, dance lessons. A lot of them home in on the small-town girls and runaways, convincing them that they're on their way to Las Vegas if they just work one more scuz bar or sleep with one more owner. Jean Valle's here. We exchange sneers, then I move away, toward Angele.

"You don't love Jean?" Angele chuckles. "Worms are great in gardens," I tell her. "Bravo. Now sit." Angele catches me in her glassy eyes and won't let go. She's fearsome at a distance, but close up, she's fragile, temperamental, opening and closing her secrets unpredictably.

"Did you ever dream of someting?" It's not really a question. "I dreamed to be a reporter, to go to Korea or de Belgian Congo. Even de Mekong Delta, but what de hell, de straight press love me. Radio Canada and Tele Metropole, even de English press want my stories when dey need someting zingy."

"Hey, Claude, François." Angele waves over a couple of cops to join us at the table. "Claude, *mon cher*," she pleads, batting her lashes. *"S'il vous plaît, deux cognac."* Angele's stories make me tingle; she knows everything about how the clubs operate, the agents, cops, the girls. Last week, she says, the Dubois shot up an east-end club. "Some poor stupid stripper was found naked, two blocks away, in de cold.

"*C'est vraiment bizarre,* eh, Claude? It was really strange when I went wit 'im and de odder cops. I see all dose single shoes under de tables. People don't tink about walking barefoot in de snow when dey're being shot at, eh?" I can imagine the room, a graveyard of shoes and the barefoot men stumbling home to their wives—"Honey, you won't believe it, but I was mugged for my shoes." I laugh to myself, enjoying the currents around me and Angele. And then her mood changes.

"So why do you do it? Why do you strip?" Angele's question unbalances me in front of the cops. "I don't know, I like the freedom, the creative part of it, I guess."

"How old are you?"

"Twenty-one," I lie.

Angele flinches and I know she wishes she were younger too. "Tank God for cognac," she says. "Or I couldn't stand getting old in dese clubs." Angele's pretty good at pressing her suggestive looks into a place and shaking its secrets loose, or getting the girls to open up their personal lives for her profiles. I think she's got something on the cops, too, the way they lean into her so attentively. Now she's trying her charm on me, as if we're part of the same conspiracy. "Don't you want to pose nude?" she keeps asking. "It will boost

your career." I don't mind the idea of doing an interview, I want to talk about my show, explain how I put
it together, the art of it. But I don't want to pose
nude—I don't even like lining up for the group shots
Angele gets us to do at these galas. I've seen girls do all
kinds of stunts to hype themselves—holding round
cards up at boxing matches, modelling bikinis at car
shows, posing for those corner-store calendars J.C.'s
got all over his office—anything to get famous or to be
on TV. I won't do it, it's stupid and fake and Angele's
part of that phoniness, maybe the centre of it. But I
can't tell her that. "Probably she's shy, *non?*" Claude
says, rescuing me.

"You like my cop friends? Dey're beautiful, eh?"
Angele pauses, stroking Claude's face, then pushing
him away. "But dey're stupid to sleep wit you girls. Just
chasing dere sex everywhere." Angele's tone is mean,
accusing, and I see her envy and her despair. "But you
like dem, don't you?" I laugh awkwardly, I don't sleep
with cops. I want to get up and walk away, but Angele
pulls me back with her eyes, sad, wet, floating ones,
making me want to protect her.

"Next week," Angele says, lurching forward, "I
will write about a go-go girl wit silicone in 'er lips, bot
sets. Can you imagine, *hasti?*" The cops down their
beers, avoiding comment. "Damn sluts—what dose
girls won't do for publicity. And de money dey're making. More in one night dan I make for one 'ole week."
Claude smirks devilishly. *"C'est simple,* Angele, just
take your clothes off too." Angele pauses, deciding

between reactions. "You wish, huh?" She turns coquettish. "Maybe I'll do a story on you." Claude and François both yelp, *"Non, non, non."* They laugh with their mouths, not their eyes, and for a sharp, brief moment I see their fear. Angele knows everything about them, the graft, the drinks, sleeping with the girls—she *could* write about them. She doesn't because she needs their attentions, because...what? It makes her feel beautiful, wanted, like us younger girls. Angele's lonely. She's also a drunk, with a sticky need to be the centre of attention. Like Sugar.

"Eh, dat's your friend, dat one, *non?"* It's Emma coming on stage with her pig. It's dressed in a miniature policeman's uniform. Now I really want to vanish. I'd warned Emma that Montreal cops don't enjoy being made fun of, especially by an alcoholic pig who drinks crème de menthe. I can tell Buster's been drinking by the green ring around his snout. It matches Emma's. The crowd is howling hysterically and Angele is laughing too, poking at Claude. His face is wooden.

Emma's dressed in hooker garb and she's snuggling Buster, pretending to seduce him so he won't arrest her. But the pig can't stand up, he's totally pissed. Buster's little legs keep splaying beneath him. The crowd is roaring with laughter, but the girls mute their reactions, watching what the cops do. François is squirming, swelling up red as an artery: "Damn pig." I don't know if he means Buster or Emma. "Dere's no business like show business," Angele cackles.

"Non, ce n'est pas correct." François springs to his feet and heads toward the owner. Three other cops have joined him. "You should tell your friend to be careful," Claude tells me. I nod stupidly. *"C'est un geste,* Claude"—it's a joke, Angele soothes but Claude taps his foot against the table. Twak. Twak, twak, twak.

"Hey, I'm not finished," Emma yells. The spotlight is fading halfway through her show. *"Bien sûr,* you're finished," François shoots back. The whole bar is watching, choosing sides, grumbling. Emma won't go peacefully, she doesn't know how. "Can't you cops take a joke?" The busboy tries to lead her off, then the owner, then François. Emma won't budge. François twists her arms backward and yanks her off stage. He says he's going to charge her with disorderly conduct or public mischief. I want to ask Angele to do something, maybe talk to her cop friend, but she's wound around Claude, having chosen her side. I guess there are some laws that can't be broken. Emma is pulled out of the club, hissing and throbbing all the way to the parking lot. I get her stuff and bring it to her. We both know she won't be allowed back into the clubs for a while.

It's crept in gradually, this solidifying of myself, this certainty. I look at the new girls now, how tender and awkward they are, how they look at me so enviously. I try to keep open to them, as Yvette and Emma did for me, explaining the rules and rituals, pointing them to the wide-open areas of striptease where they can be themselves. I remembering not knowing that once, thinking I could insert my raw self, that I could just spread out in the clubs. I didn't know how to dance, or even if it was about performance. I had no clue about the different shades of men, the fears and hurts that were hidden in those nights—how afraid Sugar was I would steal her only spotlight, that Ric couldn't love me because I wasn't injured enough, how Johnny's fury might have come from his own shame. I didn't know about the game. It *is* a game, you learn the rules, you get good at them, then you see how many you can break to stay yourself.

I'm a professional stripper now, as big and bold to these girls as Yvette once was to me. It's a powerful persona, giving me confidence and protection, as strong as armour. Sometimes I think I'm hiding behind it, that the messier parts of me are smothering inside, captive, propping up the public me. By the measurements of this place, I'm succeeding. But it makes me nervous. I wonder who I've left behind, what pieces of me.

> *Between myself and myself grows*
> *A webbed half foot,*
> *A crooked fist, a nub nose nosing*
> *up through broken ground*
> *Like a stem untangling itself....*

I don't mind working Christmas Eve at J.C.'s new club, Le Temptation. I like how the crowd thins out and the men watch so attentively. We're more transparent near Christmas, fragile in our humanness. Tonight is special. Yvette is coming, she says she has something important to tell me. I think she might start dancing again. It's crazy, I know—the girls around here are getting younger, not older. But I want to believe it, maybe because I miss her. The clubs could use her glamour, her old-world gravity. We're exhibiting too much of our surfaces, too little of our deeper, distinctive selves. The girls are so twitchy and loud now. Anyway, I've bought Yvette a silk kimono, thinking she could use it in her comeback. I wait for her, pulling the quiet around me, burying my nose in my corny Christmas book.

Slow nights are harder on the go-go girls, especially the ones who have to work Christmas Eve. The single moms and students wear their bad luck more heavily. They can't hide in the dressing room between shows as I can. I watch them clustering by the bar, creating small commotions. They circle the men like wolves, waiting for a scent of interest or a signal to bring more beer. I don't know why we don't talk to each other, why we're so divided. We don't even use the same dressing rooms—theirs is cramped, a second thought, second class. It's always been that way in Montreal. We strippers are the stars and they're the grunts.

I come out and hover alongside them, watching the men watching, observing them as they observe us. Everyone is waiting for something to happen. The porn films flicker their blue and red hues over the club, intruding on the mood. It's weird watching women give blow jobs on Christmas Eve. Yvette would hate it, we all do, how it glazes over a place. At least written porn keeps me intact—I got furious with Henry Miller's *Sexus* crap, though some of it was pretty hot. Mailer's the worst—*An American Dream* is just gross. But I can stick my own opinions in, my own experience. I can argue with it in my own mind. Visual porn is so ugly and deadening. It was the east-end bars that brought the films in first, trying to draw the men from the downtown bars. Now all the clubs have got them. *"Arrêt, donc,"* I tell Andre the barman, and for once he agrees and shuts the damn thing off. The go-gos smile gratefully and I go back to the dressing room to wait for Yvette.

Small, long-haired Manot wants to know what I'm reading, poking her head into the room nervously, not sure she's welcome. I tell her it's O. Henry's Christmas story, the "Gift of the Magi." "Would you read it for me?" she asks. *"Bien sûr."* Before I begin, Chantale wants to join us too. I paraphrase so the French girls can understand: "Della was counting the money she'd saved for her husband's Christmas present. After months of scrimping all Della had was one dollar and eighty-seven cents. She fell on the sofa and cried."

"C'est une histoire triste"—a sad story. Chantale is delighted.

"Della had only one thing to sell, the thing she loved most, apart from her husband, Jim—her brown, waist-length hair."

"Oh non," Manot sighs.

"Della raced off to Madame Sofronie who cut off her hair. Della sold it for twenty dollars."

"What are you girls doing?" "Ssssshhhhh!" Marie-France and Nicole tiptoe in and join us.

"Della searched the stores for a present worthy of her Jim. She found it finally, the platinum fob to go with his favourite watch, for twenty-one dollars. Then Della went home and curled what was left of her hair." The door creaks open and this time I see Yvette. She puts her finger to her lips and motions at me to keep reading.

"Della's husband, Jim, came home, in his worn out coat, tired. Della hoped he would still find her pretty." Manon whispers, *"J'espere"*—I hope.

"Jim's face was blank and Della was afraid she looked cheap with her short hair." The girls bridle at that. "Away *donc,* come off it," Nicole complains. "She did everyting for 'im."

"But Jim was sad. He'd bought Della a set of tortoise-shell combs for her hair, the beautiful ones she'd admired for so long in the Broadway store. The ones he couldn't afford." The girls are sorry now for judging Jim so harshly. "The poor guy," they coo.

"Della gave Jim his Christmas present, the fob. He told her then that he'd sold his watch to buy the combs." I falter here and cry. We all do, Yvette too, long slow tears dripping on our bare thighs and bellies, smudging our mascara.

"Let it be said that of all who give gifts, these two were the wisest. Of all who give and receive gifts, such as they are the wisest. Everywhere they are the wisest. They are the magi."

"Mon Dieu, le cri d'amour!" We tumble together toward our dreams, our external, professional selves shattering like eggshells. "Dat was beautiful, really," Yvette says, hugging me.

"Away, away," Andre is pounding on the door. *"Les vacances ne commencent pas. Leve tes fesses"*—get off your asses, the holiday hasn't started. The girls troop out, slow and soft with swollen eyes and Andre wonders what happened.

"L'amour," Manot tells him. "That's all."

Yvette and I are wrapped in our smiles when I hand her the Christmas present. I ask her if she's going to start dancing again. She bites her lip and doesn't answer. "What?"

"'Ere, I want you to have dis." She gives me a small brown bundle of neatly folded negligees and two or three of her dresses, long, black sequined ones I remember from Eden. They mean so much to her. I am thrilled and puzzled. "But don't you need...."

"I can't dance anymore. It's over now."

"You're not too old. Johnny was wrong."

"I wish it was like dat. I have cancer, Fonda. Breast cancer. Dey want to cut dem off."

"Oh God, Yvette."

"Don't cry, okay, because I can't take dat. Okay?"

We hold our breath, staring at each other, not daring to speak. It's the hardest silence I've ever lived. I tell her in my thoughts that I love her, that I will hold her hand forever. I tell her she is the classiest stripper I'll probably ever know and that when I wonder what is right, I think of her. Always.

Yvette gets up and hugs me tight. "I am really afraid." Her tears roll down and wet my face and I hold her long, trying to push my strength through her skin. Yvette pulls away and straightens herself. "Now dese tings I give you are silk, so don't dry clean dem. Wash dem by 'and. Wit' Woolite, okay?"

"Okay."

"Dat's it and dat's all." And she walks away in her tall, slow strut with the kimono under her arm.

Yvette disappears from me, into a world of white light and tubes where I can't follow. Montreal feels too close suddenly, too familiar, and I leave also, hurtling down the road to places I don't know, to clubs that don't know me. Rootless. Maybe it's a way of finding something, or losing it, the way I did when I was a runaway kid, a thousand years ago.

For ten weeks I work Rabitt's eastern circuit, winding through Quebec and the Maritimes: La Tuque, Rimouski, Sherbrooke, Val d'Or, Richibucto,

Moncton. Up to Wabush and Labrador City on small planes that wobble in the wind. Everywhere is wet and bald, between seasons, but the clubs are warm and steamy. I move into their newness excitedly. Often I'm alone, the only naked person for a hundred miles. Sometimes there are other strippers and we hang on to each other like vets, remembering other trenches, cackling over our victories. There are go-go girls, too, usually the washed-out ones or the renegades, sent up as punishment by Jean Valle and the other agents.

The small towns on my road tour are in need of distraction. Everyone knows who I am and what I do: the airport workers, the bus drivers. Even in the laundromats and Chinese restaurants the people recognize me and want to talk, or gawk. Maybe I'm the Big City ideal or obscenity, all the good and evil things that are spawned in the dark of Montreal. I'm never alone in these places, never unwatched, even outside in my own life. I'm lousy at puffing myself, playing the star and acting haughty as the other girls do.

The crowds are grateful I've come, for my dancing and nudity. Whole families turn out, grandmothers too, to see *la grande vedette*. They make a fuss over me, wanting to show off the best of their village or themselves, offering me tours of their mills and factories, their homes. I eat strange things, tightening my grin around pickled tongue and pig's feet. Sometimes the people are broken and I fix them with my attention more than my nakedness, with the brilliance they think I have. I like this power.

One night in Sherbrooke, an old crippled sailor offers me flowers, creasing his face so joyfully when I sit to talk with him. Every night Pierre brings me scraps of paper with his sketches of the St. Lawrence Seaway and postcards of the lakers he used to work on. He gives me his years of silence and I feel honoured.

There are poets too, and drunks who come knocking at night at my hotel door, or pitch stones at my window, whispering their dreams in warm, white clouds that float up to me. *"Danseuse, Mademoiselle Danseuse, veux-tu une toke, une scotch, un baiser?"* I see myself looking down at them in the window's reflection, surprised how much older I seem, how much bigger.

Up, up into the north I dance, sometimes not understanding the village accents or the bit-off words jabbed at me. I miss the sound of English and keep my radio close, listening to CBC—Don Harron if I'm up before noon, *As It Happens* before dinner. One day I want to meet Barbara Frum. Way the hell in Val d'Or I stumble into Ruby and we fall into a spasm of hugs and hellos, English ones. She's confident again, inside herself. She's dancing as a go-go but it's not a comedown for her. She's happy here, saving money and seeing some guy in a band at the Holiday Inn. Maybe she needs a smaller town to contain her, the comfort of familiar faces. Maybe we all do.

When I leave Val d'Or, I feel a slow sadness trickling into me, the kind I remember from the States. I feel alone, desperate to be with someone, to have another body absorb these big, silent spaces and small, hunched clubs.

I wonder sometimes what I'm doing up here, what the point is. I'm making good money, eight, nine hundred dollars a week, and the other girls' tongues wag when I tell them. I never save it, though, I spend it along the road, softening the journey, pampering myself. Money isn't interesting; it's the living, the learning, following the curve of experience. But even that dulls; places start to look alike. There's a feeling at the beginning of every town, of every week, an exhilarating blankness to paint myself into, a second chance, as fiercely renewing as wind on my face. By Saturday—sometimes as early as Tuesday—it's gone.

I begin to sleep a lot, avoiding the light and inquisitive stares. Something bad is happening to me, I think, a drowning feeling. I hurt my back in New Brunswick and straighten myself with painkillers. But the hurt stretches into Newfoundland.

I sleep a whole day in my Cornerbrook motel, down the highway from the club, groggy on the pills. I'm pulled awake by the sound of knocking. The fat man at the door has bloodshot eyes and says he knows I'm the stripper. I'm supposed to be impressed by his detective work. Mr. Pig Eyes is a salesman from the room next door and he wants to buy me a drink. I don't like how his mouth swells, how he runs his tongue over his teeth. "No," I tell him and he's indignant, as if we had some deal. He'll see me in the club, he says, and a shudder goes through me.

Pig Eyes sits in the big damp crowd of flannel shirts at O'Reilly's Bar, sending me Singapore slings. I send them back and he calls me hard to get. O'Reilly's is a plain, square room with a dance floor in the middle and tables along all four sides. There's a draft from the door, almost a gale, cramping my back and making my muscles spasm. I loosen with the pills but I can't reach into the privateness of this town, its small politeness. I can't discern the individual personalities for several nights, but they're there, watching me. It's a funny game of cat and mouse, of chins scurrying back into collars. I gradually make friends with the women who pass through the bathroom—it's where I change, my make-do dressing room.

"They're some timid, girl," the wives and girl-friends tell me. "Not used to the twirlin' and friendliness. You're some good. Best one yet." Some of them bring their drinks and stay for hours. "Jim O'Reilly thinks himself some smart for bringing in yous mainland strippers. But them other ones are nothing, just skinny things in gauzy finery, with their noses stuck in the air. Dangling themselves like jewelry until the men take a feel and O'Reilly pounds them." The women laugh caustically. "Christ, them girls were so cold the men wouldn't bed them for fear of frostbite." The women redden with embarrassment. "Not to say you're that way, if you knows what we mean."

"The Murphy boy's all goo-goo eyes for you," the women giggle. "Would rather eat his tongue, Sean would, than speak ta ya." I keep an eye out for the mysterious Sean, finding him folded into himself at the far end of the club. Night by night he moves closer. By Wednesday he sits ringside and sends me a rye and coke.

Sean Murphy's small and shy, I can tell. I help him out of his shell. Sean says the b'ys in the mill told him I was different so he'd set out for a looksee, walking all the way in the snow that battered the town from October to April. "Hell, there isn't much else to do in a payless week." Sean says he liked me right away, the way I pirouetted on stage and looked right at him. The talking makes Sean thirsty and he heaves a good three quarts down himself before he looks straight at me. "You are something," he says. I laugh, sharing the joke with the women who watch. But old Pig Eyes hovers all week, spreading his chill and meanness, and Jim can't turn him away. I feel the town curl around me, blocking him out. Jim drives me home every night. Even timid Sean shoots Pig Eyes him a cold male stare, but he keeps smirking from the edges.

My back is worsening. All week my sciatic nerve is pinching, making me smaller and stiff. I am taking too many painkillers, growing cloudy. Saturday night I want to go home right after my show. Jim drives me back and Sean comes too, looking worried, I think. They sit in my room for a beer then I go to bed and tell them to lock up. Somewhere in my sleep I hear the door closing.

I am dreaming of sounds and of shadows moving around my bed, of someone talking so softly I can't get hold of the words. I chase the sounds through dark places, catching something, someone. I can't make out his face. He says I've been looking at him, dancing for him, inviting him into my secret woman place. He pleads with me not to turn him away, he says I'm not one of those snobby girls. I dream of a hand on my mouth, of a weight on my shoulders. I push it off, I don't want this dream, I pull myself out, up, fast. I can't move, can't breathe, darkness and pressure, someone on top of me, can't breathe, get off, get off me, I'm flattening my mouth, trying to breathe from the sides, to keep my thighs tight, fighting the sharp, sharp, widening, choking, pushing, I won't scream, just get the fuck off me, off me, and then a sudden lightness and the springing back of boundaries.

Sean Murphy runs away into the night and my screams chase after him.

Sean's parents come to the club and I don't know what I'm supposed to do. They call me missus and sit there stiffly, watching me strip naked. The whole town is here, news travels invisibly as breath. They've come to see the raped stripper, what vengeance I'll claim. No one claims me, not even the women, who keep out of the bathroom, reneging on our friendship, forced back, I guess, by older duties.

It's so embarrassing, his parents sitting there like Ma and Pa Kettle, not sure where to look or which moment is more perfect to beg forgiveness for their son, blurting it out instead, the husband pushing the wife forward "because women know of such t'ings, Missus." They're so small and fragile-looking, kneading their hands, imagining I possess a dark and menacing power that the right word, the right gesture of humility, will send back. I don't know what to do or whose fault it was anymore. Bad girl, bad girl, I hear in my head. I run away, not pressing charges as the cops want me to. Let them go stare into the eyes of that mother.

I yank myself away from the glow of the TV, from drifting, forcing myself back to dance in Montreal, to anchor in the clubs again. I move into my own apartment, as if that will clean me off. But the hurt is set deep—I keep remembering the night in Cornerbrook and Sean's parents coming.

But I don't tell the girls at home that, I don't have to. I paint the night in broad, heroic strokes, exaggerating the victory of pushing the bastard off me. I don't use the word rape, it means brokenness and I am not a victim, never. I clutch my bravado and preferred truth; the clubs are generous that way, allowing me to disappear from a world I don't want, to reinvent myself after every wound, lost love, exile. It's what keeps me coming back, I guess.

Hi!
Did you forget a small place like La Tuque? It has not changed since your visit. There was a party at

the arena during ice fishing. Everybody was really smashed.

I'm not as depressed as when you met me. I often think of the fascinating conversations we had. There's no one to talk to in La Tuque. Please keep in touch.

KINDA-FONDA-YOU.

Love, Daniel

I return fiercely to the whir of the SexOHrama and the noisy acting out of women, staking my claim on home again, alongside Emma. She's back again, pig-less, and we delight in the rumours about Chesty Morgan, the American headliner who's on her way to Montreal: "Know why Chesty's feet are so small? Nothing grows in the shade!"

I'm amazed the club is so busy on Monday night. The men are lined up for half a block and the door-men are already sweaty, trying to wedge everybody in. They snarl at the go-gos to hurry up with the drinks. It's a different crowd coming to see Chesty, a lot more suits and first-timers, a snickering, bossy bunch. I don't like young suits; they think a lot of themselves and not that much of us. More and more of them have been coming these last few months. With all the com-petition, the clubs have been frantically mining new veins of cash, new kinds of customers. J.C.'s even offering free lunches, as if the suits can't afford to pay for food. The go-gos hate them, they're as cheap as Americans. They're always asking for our real names, reaching into our private layers, like a hand up a skirt, trying to feel into us. I don't tell them; my name's more personal than skin.

The clubs were friendlier before the suits descended, a lot more straightforward with the old raincoat set. Even the jocks were better than this. But the jocks won't pay a three-dollar cover. Not for a deformed set of boobs.

"Chesty Morgan: The Spirit of '76" is so big-chested she can't stand up long on stage. And she's old, her wrinkles worn smooth and soft. Cheesy Morgan, as we call her, shuffles on stage bandaged up in stars and stripes and then sits down on a chair and fiddles with her bra, or harness, or whatever that huge thing is. Her breasts completely obliterate her from the neck to the knees. She has to hold them in her arms or she'd probably tip over onto the floor. The whole club pauses, stunned. It takes Chesty thirty minutes of razzle-dazzle smoke and lights and blaring music to get to this single act of undressing. She doesn't even bother taking off her panties. Nobody could see anyway. For three weeks she turns the mood of the place dark and sniggering. Her appearance is an occupation, souring the club with the pasty, contemptuous faces of her businessman crowd.

The local girls are stiffening against J.C. and the intrusions on our home. It's not just Chesty but his muscling around the new nudity law. Now that we're allowed to take off our G-strings, J.C. has been pushing the girls to do spreads. The strippers don't want to, but some of the go-go girls are already at it, getting up on stage for their three skimpy songs and blowing the suits away with their spreads. These are not good spreads, not artistic the way Ruby used to do. This is wham, bam, breakfast, ma'am. One girl even got her vulva pierced; another one's shaved her entire pubic area. Now *Sextra* is featuring colour photographs of go-gos and Angela's hardly talking to us strippers anymore. The go-go girls are smirking, enjoying their new claim on the audience's attention. Even the second-rate strippers are starting to do spreads. Standard contracts are being rewritten, not just by J.C., but by all the club owners and agents, so that out-of-town strippers have to do spreads.

But I won't do it, no way—not just because I think it's raunchy, but because I don't want to be told what to do, I don't want to be invaded. I feel it as hard as a fist in me, definite. I try to talk to the girls, to organize them—if we all refuse, what can the clubs do? But they're hesitant, afraid, whispering like criminals, small in their fear. I don't keep pestering them. For weeks I'm sweaty about how I'll say no all by myself, about what might happen. I've barely imagined living on the outside, I don't know what I'd do there. I've watched girls try to leave and then come back, cursing the narrowness of other places. I've seen some get married to greasy, simple men, or leave with rich guys for faraway dreams. The blonder girls have gone off to work in Japan, the plainer ones to restaurants. Everybody has her plan, her clothing boutique or small hotel, her Hollywood contract and Las Vegas shows that hover somewhere in the distance, near old age. Or fallen-breast time. I think I might be a writer or poet, or maybe a talk show host. But these thoughts drift like rings of smoke, changing shape and fullness, always evaporating Out There, in the unknown vastness at the edge of the cliff.

I catch J.C. in the space between day and evening shifts, in the quiet time when he listens to the girls' confessions and pats them softly. Babette's inside, sobbing theatrically about why she keeps forgetting to charge her boyfriend for drinks. I march in after her, cranked at full throttle, blasting J.C. about his obligations to art, about being like Medici and needing to nurture artists. "Doing spreads is not a creative act," I spit. A small grin wriggles on J.C.'s face. "But dis is a business and dis is what my customers want."

"Not everybody wants to see girls spread, and they have rights too." J.C. chuckles. "And stop laughing, J.C., I'm serious, okay?" He shrugs bemused. "I'm royally pissed off. I didn't come here to spread and you wanted me just fine when I didn't do them. If that's what you want then I'll have to...."

"Dat's okay, Fonda," he says, waving his hands. "You don't 'ave to if you don't want." I collapse a little, not expecting such an abrupt victory. "So what about the other girls who don't want to do it?" I press my luck.

"Dat's between me and God and dem."

"Come on, J.C."

"I cannot change de laws of business." Neither can the strippers. One by one the girls capitulate, even Emma, grumbling, until only Nikki the Vampire Girl and I are left. I wear my stuck-together thighs as a badge of honour, and it both irks and inspires the other girls.

Tits for Tots

THINGS THAT I WOULD LIKE TO DO:

dance every four weeks

get poetry published

write interviews for newspapers

act in theatre and film

I tiptoe quietly into the small stairwell on rue de Park, not wanting anyone to see me or to notice my shabby portable typewriter. I move like a thief, filling the place with my own secrets. I feel more naked than I do on stage, more open to derision. This is my studio, my *artist's studio.* I've read that Hemingway did it this way. I will learn to write here, I will dance only once every four weeks, maybe every six, if I can afford it. I will write until I learn how or until my fingers fall off. I will be a poet first and then maybe a journalist, novelist, playwright. I will learn to learn, to watch and to understand. I will read every poetry book I can buy and I will give myself one year to know this place. Already I'm calling my boyfriends lovers and trying to smoke Gitanes. They're awful.

I attend poetry readings and gallery openings regularly, meeting poets and actors and artists. They're a lot like strippers, outside of things, but ferociously internal. I meet Martin, who's written a book, and Don, who's written two. There's Ingrid the sculptor, Derek and Mort the filmmakers, Bobby the pouting Irish poet, Clara the lesbian and her radio friend Matthew, and the actor, Peter. I like Peter; he's got a beautiful, chiseled face and explains foreign films in an English, Beatles accent.

They are strange to me, these artists, complicated and gigantic. I listen to them hunched in dark corners, discussing the death of Steve Biko, Lina Wertmuller's *Seven Beauties,* Michel Tremblay, cursing always their own bad luck with landlords, arts grants, agents. I am thrilled by what they know. But being a stripper makes me an oddity, even among them. The men are curious at first, or afraid, imagining my powerful sexuality, wanting to worship my public freedoms; their lovers and wives are more suspicious. They worry I'll steal their men, and when I don't, or do without their knowing, they whisper questions, asking me where to buy fishnet stockings or how to take their clothes off gracefully. Women and men both have boring ideas about striptease, maybe the same ones I used to have. They think it's an instinctive, swelling urge like nymphomania, something ferocious that drains the blood out of a women's brain, leaving her feeble-minded and primitive. They don't recognize the performance elements, the business complexities, the guts it takes to manoeuvre around people's expectations every night.

Clara asks me if I feel exploited by stripping and the question startles me. Exploitation is about poor people with lunch buckets working in factories, workers who get stiffed for their pay or for their hours. I'm making close to a thousand dollars a week, I don't have to eat tofu or stuff food in *my* purse at *vernisages* and launches. I'm not exploited. How can I be when I'm assigned such mystery and power? When her friend Matthew thinks I'm amazing. Have I ever read Marx or Engels, Clara asks, and gives me them to look at. Straight people, even artists, assume a right to judge, an invasion of privacy that club people never demand. It's part of what makes stripping so beautiful—we don't have to explain ourselves to each other, we invent ourselves without questions. Maybe it's a liability too. Things keep repeating themselves in the clubs, and we stay still in a strange kind of way.

I claim my new world of poetry, its startling pureness. It claims me back, erasing time, taking me to internal places. Some poems I read have the glitter of rhinestones, like American dancers, stunning in their stylish, empty beauty. Emily Dickinson and her old-lady poems sear with an ache and wisdom that reminds me of Yvette. The Beats are Emma: the pounding, fragmented words of Ferlinghetti and Ginsberg; Sylvia Plath, too. But I love the Imagists best, the short, lean lines, the folded-in meanings, the immediate grab at my heart. I say their poems out loud, hearing myself saying them, owning them, then I plunge back into my words:

Caught in the midnight, middle place
Between my faces, twitching,
itching, curling like a snake,
Like a fake among the perfect ones
Before myself and after,
Looking for my name.

I do my writing privately, almost sneakily, no one asks about it, not the strippers or the artists, and I hover between the two worlds, stranded by my lack of language, my inability to explain myself because I'm not wholly invented yet. I learn how to write poetry submissions, and to wait for answers; they come slowly, always exciting me: *Branching Out*—no, *Canadian*

Forum—no, *Columbia Pictorial, Exile, Fireweed, The Living Message, Matrix, Ms., Origins, Portico, Quarry*—no, no, no.

It takes patience, this writing and mailing, a constant postponement of other urges. It's hard to stay still every day, and alone, to write in solitary confinement. I'm not used to silence or to this lack of distraction. I miss performing, the immediate gratification and definateness of being. I feel a need for it like food.

I stop shaving my legs and armpits, like the other artists do, and when I go back to the clubs, the owners and men are stunned. "Wanna see something female?" I yell to the crowd, and they howl back, thinking I'll spread my legs. "Here, take a whiff," and I lift up my arms to show them my hair. I love the shock on their faces.

Emma and I are are so tangled in our history, we're chafing against each other now, growing differently. She resents my confidence, I think, and my other life. Emma's bristling at my new friends and at the other strippers, especially Black Sheba.

Sheba's one tough nut. I've been circling her for months, trying to sneak into a friendship. She's kept her distance from us girls, maybe because we're white, or because she doesn't understand French. I'd see her at a lot of clubs and galas, holding her head high, oblivious to the girls' suspicions around her, to the rumours that she is a prostitute—Emma says that about anybody she's afraid of. Sheba is regal, I think, independent—she doesn't need my company or approval. It takes persistence to get through her aloofness, and lots of dangling questions. We become friends cautiously, with ambiguous nods and agreements.

Beneath Sheba's poise is a fierce determination and a certainty of herself. She works the clubs the way I do, the way Emma used to, making them fit around her, refusing anything they force on her. Sheba sees through the game, she hates the conniving of Jean Valle. American girls like Sheba come up freelancing, but he claims a chunk of their salary from the clubs as his commission. They're not even his girls, but he takes his fifteen-percent cut. Most dancers accept it as the cost of doing business, but Sheba's worked New York and Chicago; she's smart, fearless. She harangues Valle constantly, marching up to him and demanding her money back. Sometimes he gives it to her, sometimes he doesn't.

Black Sheba, Princess of the Nile, is beautiful as a model, and always well made up, even in daylight. She wears perfect plastic fingernails, long as talons. Sheba groans at my plain face and chewed-up fingers, calling my clothes "trailer park trash." I laugh. I don't care about my daytime image, I like discarding my stripper self and melting into normalness, into jeans and T-shirts and fat, woolly sweaters. Sheba wears shiny clothes on the street, along with high leather boots and tight, plunging blouses. "Dress like a fox,

girl, get a fox." Sheba is a prostitute, though she doesn't
tell me, I have to guess, just like I guess she has something going with JC. Sheba confirms her prostitution
vaguely, avoiding the word. "If I gonna shake my
black booty, girl, I gonna make me lots of money."
Sheba calls it dating and I think of Ken and Barbie.
She says she doesn't give a spit what people think,
including me. I don't believe her. It's supposed to be
the right of strippers to look down on whores, to
assert our superiority: "Look, fella—at least I'm not a
whore." I know I could never be one, I couldn't make
myself invisible enough to suit men that way.

Stripping's about being gigantic, about performance and force—whores are supposed to dissolve
themselves into the needs of men, transfusing their
power to their tricks. But Sheba's sturdier than the
street girls I've seen. Men swarm around her when we
go to the discotheques together, picking up her scent,
following her nervously. She sits at the best tables,
perched like a queen, muttering her appraisals at me:
a "Shriners' convention" when the pickings are poor,
"a gold rush" when there's a current of potential in a
place. Sheba says a girl can't go to a good place alone,
so she brings me along. My job is to scare off the losers
by telling them I'm a sociology student doing research
on dating. Sometimes I'm Sheba's translator: "Tell tha'
boy to cut the French if he wanna talk ta me"; "Ask
him what kinda car he drive." Many nights Sheba disappears on the arm of a rich admirer, or sometimes

with Gaetan, the staff sergeant at the local division. She always offers to pay my cabfare home and makes me promise to call her when I get there.

I hound Sheba with questions about how she got into hooking, what she does when guys don't pay, what her weirdest trick was. It makes her laugh, though sometimes she curls her lip in warning, as if she thinks I'm judging her. I try not to. Sheba says prostitutes are more honest about the business of selling their bodies and that strippers are the frauds and candy-asses, teasing men and then retreating into their fake virginity. Maybe, but I'm selling more than that. I'm a performer.

The whole idea of a good show is ownership and presence, I think, filling the club with me, not just my nakedness. Sheba's the same way, forcing her personality on dates and imposing her own morality—she won't go with men who have young families, or with drunks. So what's honesty and what's illusion? What's ours and what's theirs, or is it all related? Sheba calls her work by other names, wraps herself in beautiful clothes, invents a higher class of prostitution. Maybe I'm doing the same thing on stage, creating only shades of difference imperceptible to those male eyes out there. I don't know if the clichés apply or not. I'd hate them calling me a whore and Sheba wouldn't like being called that either.

Sheba's prostitution gradually becomes a small and ordinary fact between us, receding into the other

details of our friendship. For all her high-class world-
liness, She's got no sense for art or culture, no curios-
ity. Her idea of poetry is the inside of a Hallmark
birthday card—she says my stuff's bad because it
doesn't rhyme. I try pulling her into the beauty of the
Imagists, into the circle of my artist friends. Sheba
says she doesn't like them because they're cliquish.
What really bothers her, I think, is their drinking beer
instead of Remy Martin. Being poor is the worst kind
of failure to Sheba, choosing it is unthinkable. Maybe
it has to do with growing up black in a fatherless
home. Sheba barricades herself against those leaner
times with clothes and jewelry. She's a hoarder; I've
seen her buy cartons of toothpaste and dish soap on
sale, things she couldn't use in a lifetime. She gives a
lot away, too, to children's charities and foreign relief.
Making money and spending it is Sheba's passion, a
kind of insurance, I guess. She thinks I'm nuts for not
caring for that stuff.

Sheba says my problem is that I'm too brainy and
read too much—there's no future in it. I should be
accumulating wealth, cashing in on my youth before it
gets away from me. I could start by shaving my legs:
"It took us thousands a years to drop outa the trees.
You look like you still in one, girl." She warns me not
to turn into Emma. Into a dyke, she means. That's
what Sheba calls her, but I don't know if it's true, and
I don't care.

Emma and Sheba are like cats together, all hissy
and clawed. "That girl's some sorry white ass," Sheba

tells me. "You gotta get yerself some new friends."
She's right about Emma. Emma looks like a member
of the Baader-Meinhof gang in her fatigues and army
boots; she's not funny anymore, just angry, always
angry. She won't reinvent herself, won't accept that
clubs don't want artists any more, or poetry. They
want girls to be the same now, to do identical routines.
Every part of the show is a prelude to the spreads. I
still won't do them, but I've had to work harder to dis-
tract the men from their expectations, to keep them
from feeling cheated. I've got to swell up big in myself
to occupy that stage. I have my own fans now, regulars
who call me the Don Rickles of burlesque because of
my sassy tongue. Emma doesn't. She goes on stage and
tells the guys what they're spending on tits and ass
could feed a Central American village.

I try to coax Emma back into her humour, hiding
rubber snakes in her shoes, gluing falsies to her bras,
but she glowers at me, putting a hard face between us,
calling me a moron and a sellout. Me? For all her yak
about organizing and woman power, I was the one
who refused to do spreads—she buckled under the
pressure.

"The feminists are right, you know," Emma says.
"They should shut these places down." Sheba laughs.
"They should walk you on a leash, girl." We've been
hearing a lot about feminists, their rants in the paper
about how they're going to stop female exploitation,
how they want to protect strippers and hookers, as if
we're victims. As if they know anything about us. They

sound like those evangelical Bible bigots from the southern U.S.

If Emma really thinks things are so bad in the clubs, she should change them from the inside. She could stop the porn films, the spreads, the agents' larcenies, if she got out from behind her pulpit. But I lose Emma in these vague, circling arguments, she's not listening. She won't come to poetry readings anymore, or to my studio or to meet my artist friends. She's sealing herself shut—the more she hates the clubs the more she sinks into them and away from other kinds of light. It's almost as if she's scared.

There's a brief and sudden peace between Emma and me, a week of profound truce. "You were right," Emma howls one day. "There is a fucking God." Fat-Ass Gladys, Eden's Gladys, arrives at the SexOHrama as a stripper, a bad one. She works the day shift so she never gets to see us. Emma and I gloat all week, coming in early and peeking from the balcony at her in her cheesy costumes and starlet conceit—Gladys keeps ordering the busboy to retrieve her costumes, as if she owns the place. She can't dance, she grinds—pivoting hips, thrusting pelvis, hands behind her head in some 1950s poster pose. She's too short and stubby to make it work, too twitchy on coke to linger through the undressing. She yanks things off too quickly. Nobody likes her.

When we finally poke into the dressing room, Gladys is fragile and vacant. She fumbles into a desperate familiarness, talking, hugging, pleading with dark eyes for friendship.

"Hey, hey, fabulous Gladys," Emma chirps.

"Wow, it's great to see you girls. Did you, uh, did you see my show?"

"The guys love it," Emma says mockingly. "Heard they wanted to hire you for a private party. A thousand bucks, I think."

"Really?"

There's a strange and reliable justice in the clubs, a certain comeuppance, we believe in like religion. But there's something ugly about justice too, about history catching up to people. Emma doesn't need to be mean.

"Yeah. They said they'd give you two thousand if you'd let them film ya."

"That's amazing."

"Three thousand for a couple of blow jobs."

Gladys wavers. "You're kidding, right?"

God, I can remember wishing Gladys would get hit by a bus when I was at Eden, or be eaten by Sugar's snake. I watch her being swallowed now, the hurt filling up her eyes. "She's kidding, Gladys," I tell her. I lie to Gladys and tell her it's a tough club and that maybe she shouldn't be stripping here.

"Sure, she should," Emma coaxes.

"Stop it, Emma."

"Fuck off."

Gladys turns away from me, preferring the sharper edges of Emma's attentions, not seeing through them, not wanting to. Gladys lasts a week. Maybe she's heading for another club, a second chance. Months later I hear that her family had her kidnapped and taken back to Lebanon to live a decent life.

After Gladys, the armistice is over. Emma disconnects from me, or me from her. I don't care. She retreats into her scowls, repeating the same old whine—striptease is dead, we've all become whores. Sheba's offended by that: "Only the good ones, girl." Emma fades away, appearing briefly at the edges of my new friendships, at other clubs, in bookstores, among the Maoists at the end of peace marches, then finally disappearing. I think the last time I see her is at Bar Maurice, the Dubois place, howling her poetry at a derisive French biker crowd. She acts too busy to talk to me, but when I'm leaving she grins and says, "See ya, kiddo." It was what she used to call me, and maybe her way of saluting our friendship.

It's a relief to see Emma go. I don't know why she stayed, drowning in her hate, stubborn in it, unable to move with or against the currents of these clubs. It was a kind of suicide, I think, her wanting to go but not knowing how, making herself despised so that she was forced out. I won't miss her, but I'll always yearn for her genius. I remember her wearing those damned antlers, screeching out her insults at Eden, opening my mind to what I could be, to the absence of borders. She made the men notice her, made them pay attention. Who's going to pull their eyes open now, their minds? Or is that part over? I feel suddenly alone, old, as if I've lived long enough to see something come and go, to know it won't come back. The future seems closer somehow, but I'm still hazy inside it, still incomplete. A vagueness settles on me, something menacing. I think it's dread. Or grief.

For weeks the girls have been buzzing excitedly, fastening their admiration to me, making me gigantic. Everyone wants to know about my showdown with Valle—they tug at me to tell them, again and again, and almost every night I do.

It wasn't something I planned, I tell them. I was just feeling fed up with Valle, annoyed to have to complain with Sheba about the commission business again. But Valle wouldn't give the money back; he said it was the cost of protection. The girls cluster around me, rolling their eyes and groaning.

"If I want protection, I'll pay for my own pimp," Sheba told him. Valle didn't like that. His smile twitched and he tried to shove past her. "Give her the money," I told him. Then he turned to me and said, "Out of the way, you stupid bitch." The girls let go a low growl. "I don't let people call me that," I tell them. "I stuck my foot out and tripped the bastard on his blind side." The girls nod slowly, imagining Valle on the floor, his wriggling like a worm, savouring it. I was still shaking when he pulled himself up and widened his one good eye at me, saying how he was going to get me and Sheba. Fuck him, he wasn't my agent, what did I need him for?

"Get out of here, I told him."

"Yeah," the girls shout, jeering. "Get out of here, fuck off, *mange de la merde, maudit Cyclops."* They're so brave in their imaginations, putting the boots to him.

Then Sheba, Princess of the Nile, stepped in, towering over him like an Amazon. "And on your way out," she says, "get yourself a dick. Most men have one." The room breaks out in yelps and whooping, the girls bang their shoes and hair brushes on the counter, slapping their hands all over Sheba and me.

Still, I sense something flimsy about my victory—nothing's really changed. I knew when Valle walked away it wasn't finished. For a few weeks, I can't work the other clubs, Valle's warned them not to book me. The girls think it adds to my heroism, but I feel shrunken in myself. I keep rewinding that night in my mind, playing it back in slow motion, freezing it in parts. I can see the doormen skulking in the background, pretending not to see me, and the strippers, too, moving out of the way. Even Sheba looks scared in slow motion—turning away, trying to get out of there. And me, I'm heaving like a project girl, all fists and spit and scruffiness. Only Valle seems assured, even in his rage, grinning with certainty that he can get us back. No matter how I play that night—for the girls or for myself—it's the same old story, the same old winners and losers. I don't know how to get out from under the repeating defeat. Sheba doesn't know either, doesn't really care when I talk to her about it.

"We done good, we beat him once," she says. "You wanna change the world? Girl, you sound like the old

Coke commercial: "I'd like to teach the world to sing in perfect harmony.'" Sheba thinks I should be content with a good story and one brief triumph, but I'm not. I miss Emma fiercely. She'd see through this, she'd put words on what I'm feeling.

I wish I could tell Emma about Clara's books I'm reading, the big ones with tiny print, about factory workers in the last century turning into machines and getting beat by their bosses. They're making me see a connection between us girls, that stripping is a job and we're all workers. I used to think stripping was about art and that artists were individuals, like Emma, answering only to their higher impulses. It was the other, weaker girls who were the robots, workers— doing what they were told and crouching in themselves. If I got good enough I wouldn't become them, I thought, I wouldn't have to manoeuvre around those names: bitch, whore, stupid. I worked out my deal with J.C., the things I would and wouldn't do on stage, the weeks I'd work, the agents I'd work with. I got above the grimier details, earning the privilege, but Valle and the books take me into another understanding, into my relatedness to the other girls. I can't escape my context, surroundings—we're bound together by this place.

I don't know what single thing could bring us strippers and go-gos together, make us feel attached. We need something to bring our nerve and pride back, our ownership. I know this as surely as if I've been here before.

I am drifting through the crack between waking and sleeping, hovering at my secret place. It's autumn here, not summer when children die or disappear—it's the new school year with the starchy feel of hope, the sounds of braces creaking, wheelchair tires humming, pushed by the force of stronger legs, by laughter—our laughter, not the hissing sound of pity, or the muffled whispering of aversion, embarrassment, horror that protrude sharply from the world. We aren't freaks here, we are bodiless, pure light dancing and braiding together.

When I swim back up to wakefulness, I know precisely how to organize the women.

I look up the children's charities listed in the phone book, trying to find some place to take the money I'm going to raise. I'm planning to organize a charity event for crippled kids; I'm going to make us proud of ourselves.

"That's right, we're a group of dancers," I say, over and over, into the phone.

"The ballet?" they ask.

"Strippers."

"You mean...*topless* strippers?" They say they can't, they won't. They say they'll call me back and never do. I sit for a week beside the phone. Finally the children's hospital sounds interested. It needs the money for the Christmas drive to buy children's toys. My heart is pounding. They'll have to talk it over, it's a whole new direction—I understand, thump, thump. Can they meet with me? Yes! They say they're worried about their reputation—mine, they mean. They're probably

imagining me as Dolly Parton or Loni Anderson—
whore with a heart of gold, busting out of a blue ango-
ra sweater. I wonder how to counteract their clichés, if
I should wear a pleated skirt, or my jeans and sweater.
Maybe I should just prance in with one of Sheba's
sparkly get-ups or some pasties glued to the outside of
my shirt.

Now I have to plan an event, find a venue, get the
girls. I'll have to negotiate around the agents, oh God,
and Valle. At least the other clubs are booking me
again. I think the charity show should be a gala, an
old-fashioned burlesque review with strippers, comics,
hosts—a twelve-hour strip-a-thon—hell, that's almost
fifty strippers. At first the girls are shocked, thinking I
want them to dance for the kids. I have to keep repeating that we're raising *money* for the kids, for their
Christmas toys. Once they understand, the girls melt.
I go to the other clubs and talk in the dressing rooms.
Will you do it, I ask. *"Ah, les pauvres enfants, bien sûr."*
"Why not, it's Christmas." "Me, I do it for my brud-
der, 'e 'ad polio." It's always from their hearts. I knew
it would be.

"But where are we going to do it?"—I don't know
yet. "'Ow are we going to get back for our regular
show?" I don't know that either.

Jean Valle is a problem. He can see more with his
one good eye than most people can with two. "I'm
watching you," he says when I run into him. "Don't
put ideas in de girls' heads." What ideas, I ask, fishing.
"I'm de one makes de galas around here. Dese are my

girls." I know all I have to do is apologize to him, but I can't. He starts blocking my way into the clubs again, sending chilly warnings. The girls are nervous now; they start phoning me back, saying they can't do a show. Some are afraid to talk to me, afraid they'll look like collaborators. It only hardens my resolve.

"Watch your back, girl," Sheba warns me. She thinks what I'm doing is nuts. A couple of Valle's favourite strippers start a rumour that I'm planning to steal the money I raise. I start pushing back. "Nobody's making money on this but the kids," I tell them. "And Valle, if he ever got his hands on it." I focus my efforts on the girls who have kids: Tiny Tina and Happy Daze. "Don't you want to do one remarkable thing in your life?" I ask. "Something you can tell your kids you're proud of?" They both sign up.

I can't find a club willing to do it, they all want to make money—the door, the bar. They want to squeeze me into raising funds by selling buttons and posters; I'd be lucky to make two hundred dollars. Even J.C.'s ambivalent. He's afraid of agent trouble and of the whole thing flopping. He's got the best club in Montreal and he doesn't want to look bad. J.C. doesn't understand how I can get fifty strippers on stage in a single day. "I can't get six strippers to show up on time," he complains.

"Okay, what if I sign up at least half the strippers?" He shakes his head. "How about reporters? What if I can guarantee television, radio and newspaper coverage? Imagine the publicity."

"I'm trying. But dis is a nude show, dere not going to put dat on de television.

"Come on, J.C., I know I can do it."

"I don't tink it's possible. I'm sorry."

J.C. was my best hope, my only one. I call Clara's friend Matthew, who works in radio, for help. He thinks it's a great idea and that everyone would cover it. How do I get them to come, I ask. "Write a press release." What's a press release?

For several nights my cab is followed home by the same black Lincoln and the same three thugs. They don't talk to me or do anything, they just park outside my apartment and smoke cigarettes. I pretend I don't see them.

Every club I work, every night I work, I badger the girls to sign up, sneaking around the doormen and managers, talking in hushed tones like I'm a thief. With all the fear and cancellations, I've only got four strippers confirmed. I'm growing doubtful. I tell the girls about the creeps following me home. I say again tonight that we've got to stop flinching, that we're not victims or whores. "I'm gonna help these kids if I have to dance every show for twelve hours myself." The girls say nothing. I'm so exhausted I feel like crying. I stare at them in the mirror, wondering how I can reach them, what it takes to stop people from being afraid. Somebody starts to giggle, then someone else. What, what?

Dolly hands me a small wad of bills. "It's from all of us for the kids," she says. "We couldn't take you dancing for twelve hours." The rest of the girls shriek with laughter, then sign their names to my list. It's a turning point, the building up of a magnetic force that pulls other girls in. After tonight there's an electric whispering across the clubs, a growing conspiracy among the girls to join in.

"Girl, what the hell you gonna name this thing if it gets going?" Sheba teases me. I guess Celebration of Nudity isn't cutting it with her. "How 'bout Tits for Tots?" I offer. "I said you couldn't write." Tits for Tots is what we girls start calling it.

I go back to J.C. with a list of fourteen interested reporters that I've made up, and the promises of twenty-seven strippers. He throws his hands in the air, "Enough, enough. Okay." He's agreeing, he's going to let me use his club. I lock on to J.C. and hug him hard; for the first time ever, strippers are going to be running the show. This is history, something for the *Guinness Book of Records.* "You 'ave de door but I want de bar. And don't charge more dan tree dollars. I don't want de regulars to be scared off."

"You're okay, J.C. For an owner."

"You too. For a stripper."

It's real. I have five weeks to organize the charity. I'm gaining momentum now, pleading with comics and professional MCs to be part of the show—it's easy to beg when it's not for yourself. Girls are calling me up, too, wanting to be included, swelling up in their courage and ignoring Valle. He's still threatening to ban any of them who join up, but he corners me

outside the SexOHrama, saying he'll help for half the
cut. I want to tell him to piss off, but I thank him for
the generous offer and leave him dangling.

There are so many details to work out: schedul-
ing, hosts, press releases, transportation. Almost all the
girls will be coming from and going back to other
clubs. I can't expect them all to take taxis. I ask Sheba
to work on Gaetan, the staff sergeant. Maybe the cops
can chauffeur the girls. Sheba's still thinks I'm crazy,
but she says she'll try. "I'll do it for the kids. I gotta little girl back home."

"You do?" After two years of knowing Sheba, it's
the first time she's ever mentioned it. "Yeah, she lives
with my mother in Chicago." Sheba doesn't want to
say much more, I think it makes her sad.

"You know what you said about being proud of
something?"

"Yeah?"

"Well...you know."

"Yeah, I know, Sheba."

"And don't you send them reporters to all those
sorry-ass white girls. I wanna front-page picture to
help with business."

"If I get desperate."

"Girl, you don't deserve me."

The week before the gala is a jumble of chores and
demands—I'm scared stupid but I can't show it. The
press releases really work, I'm doing French and
English interviews all over the place, and some of the
other girls are too. The reporters seem surprised that

we can talk so well and want to know why we're doing it. "Because we want to contribute," I tell them. "Because it's our way of belonging to the bigger community." It's amazing to be saying these things in public, to be talking in a clear voice. I feel good, big, smart.

The girls like hearing themselves on radio, like reading about themselves in the newspapers, enjoy being treated with respect. Every day we buy copies of *La Presse, The Montreal Star, The Gazette, Le Devoir, Sextra,* scanning them for stories about us, howling to each other when we find one. The girls are preparing their best shows, getting all polished up. Even I buy something sparkly to wear for the night.

Sheba and Dolly and Tiny and I spend a weekend festooning the club in Christmas decorations. The night before the gala we make salads and arrange platters of cold cuts for the media. I don't know if it's the way you're supposed to do it, but I figure the reporters are coming into our home and we'll treat them like guests. I only hope they don't think it's too shabby, or die of food poisoning. "You're sure the mayonnaise in the potato salad'll last twelve hours?" I ask Sheba.

The press start arriving at noon, finding places for their news cameras, or just hovering around the food and the girls in the dressing room. I'm clutching a clipboard, answering everybody's questions, worrying about details, telling Sheba to do this and that. She's my lieutenant today. The comics start arriving, and the hosts, ordering their cognacs. By two there's a line-up forming outside in the snow and the doormen are glistening with sweat, weighted down with tips already. The club starts to fill up with noise and heat, with a slow-building roar. Dozens of go-gos are darting through the club with drinks. I can see J.C. looking content at the bar, nose in the air as if he's smelling money.

Finally the girls start arriving in their furs and big hats, strutting in their cool, pretending to be stars. Their poise slides off in the dressing room and they let loose their shrieks and delight: "Holy shit, it's big!" Some I have to swat away from the reporters, warning them not to give out their home phone numbers. Even the cops are smiling, dragging the girls' bags like bell-hops. Twenty of them are chauffeuring the strippers back and forth in their cruisers. Dolly says it's the first time she's been taxied by a driver who knew the city.

There's such a warm, pulsing glow, a sense of shared goodness. Borders evaporate between strippers and go-gos, girls and management, suits and strippers, cops and everyone else. This is Christmas. *"Mesdames et messieurs, pour la première fois,* the strippers of Montreal present the first annual Celebration of Nudity." All day and night the people come, the reporters linger, the girls twinkle in their pride, dancing their best shows, shaking donation cans through the crowds, kissing men for a dollar. I even get interviewed by Barbara Frum! It's not an accident, I had a

friend call the *As It Happens* radio tip line. Barbara
doesn't have that disdainful tone she has for people she
doesn't agree with. She gets a kick out of talking to a
stripper, and she sounds really moved. Some of the
other press are not so charming, especially the photographers. They keep wanting lewd poses and some
of the girls are eager, thinking it's their ticket to stardom. Sheba and I don't like the girls being made fools
of. Sheba distracts one guy as I accidentally spill beer
on the camera around his neck. When another
reporter engages us in a serious conversation about
strippers being prostitutes, Sheba berates him so loudly he sputters out apologies and leaves. But most of the
press see something good in us; even Angele from
Sextra is emotional. She clasps on to me, her red,
drunk face all damp with tears. "Dat's beautiful," she
sputters. Jean Valle pops in and makes a big show of
shaking my hand and getting his picture taken beside
me.

As the show goes on and the fear inside me loosens,
I watch the girls closely, how they seem to unfold from
their own hard wariness. I see them collecting each
other's costumes, running errands, helping the go-gos
with the drinks—forbidden in normal times. The customers also sense something deeper, more decent in us
and themselves; they move out of our way without
grumbling, cheer on even the clumsiest girls, empty
their pockets. They're caught in their assigned roles
too, and I see how relieved they are to be human. We

are all free of shame and guilt tonight. I wonder if
Yvette has seen me on TV, if Emma has—I hope so. I
want them to know this gala is for all of us who
dreamed of being whole and acceptable.

At the end of the night I take the stage to offer my
thanks and to announce how much we've raised. The
place is still crammed with people, but there is a sudden hush as their wet, warm faces look up at me. It's
the first time I've been up here fully clothed. My voice
is raspy, wobbling with emotion. We've made two
thousand, fifty-six dollars and twenty-nine cents, I tell
the crowd. They roar with approval, as I stand there
blinking back my tears and smiling. Sheba comes on
stage to steady me, then the strippers, the doormen,
the cops and go-gos, all of us hugging and swaying to
the strains of "Gens de pays." We are bodiless, pure
light dancing and braiding together, extinguishing the
darkness at our edges.

The Beautiful Fonda Peters,
When I didn't receive a reply fore years ago I
figured you couldn't be bothered because you
probably got many letters because you are such
a pretty girl. Now I can see you have been busy.

Congratulations are in order. Yesterday you
made the news all the way to Calgary. The fund
raising campaign you organized in Montreal for
the hospital rated enough to be mentioned along
with a taped interview.

Since it is over, perhaps you might find a few minutes so you could sit down and write me a letter. Remember I asked for a picture as well if you care to send me one. All the very best.

Your friend, Harold

CHAPTER 8

The Bump, the Grind

I am catapulted into another orbit after my gala suc-
cess, yanked into a widening world. I am not just a
stripper anymore, I'm a spokeswoman. I should think
about that, but there's no time, I'm pulled along by the
grab of celebrity. At first I like the attention—the girls
looking up to me, journalists doing long articles on
me for weekend magazines, every film and journalism
student wanting me to star in his school project. I'm
invited as a celebrity to the Big Brothers' bowl-a-thon.

I also get a call from a porn producer wondering if I'd be interested in film work. He says he saw me on TV but I guess he missed the part where I said I was sick of being thought of as a floozy.

I'm accepting invitations to speak at universities, though they seem surprised when I want to be paid. The students are my age but they call me "miss" and "ma'am," imagining I am older and more worldly, I guess. I talk to them about my right to work the clubs, my right to be accepted, and they cheer. They like me saying how great striptease is, they seem to crave those absolutes, especially the boys. It's as if I'm conspiring with them, defending their rights too. I feel annoyed they don't ask me more about Tits for Tots, that their questions are stupid: where do I get my costumes, am I a prostitute, do I date customers? "No one making less than thirty thousand," I tell them, and they take me seriously. I start to think these guys might be suits in the making. When I try explaining the working conditions in the clubs or the power of the agents and our need to organize, the guys get restless and disconnect from me. The girls home in on the moral stuff. They want to know if we have to sleep with bosses, the amount of control we have over our shows, if we feel disgusted by men looking at our bodies. I can tell by their tone they think I'm exploited. I can't interest them in our complexities, our wounds and accomplishments. This spokeswoman business really demands pat answers, but I love ambiguity, the freedom it suggests. It's what I get in the clubs, the magical ingredient that no one in the straight world seems to understand.

Fame is confusing. I start to wonder if I want this publicity. I like the anonymity of stripping, the licence to reinvent myself, the lack of explanations. There's a spontaneity that exists in there that doesn't out here. Being a celebrity doesn't make me lighter, as I thought; it's more like an acquiring of thicker skins, defences. I'm becoming a symbol of something and it's as different as the people who assign it to me. To my Jewish fruit-store owner who puts my newspaper picture by the cash, I'm a do-gooder. To the college students, I'm the high priestess of nonconformity. The pornographers think I'm a whore, and for my Greek neighbour, Maria, who stares at my twinkling G-strings on the clothesline, I'm a radical, new world feminoid, someone free who wafts above her possibilities.

Sheba says if I were in the United States, I'd have a personal manager getting me on the *Donahue* show by now. And do what? People are crazy for fame. They think I should be grateful for it, that I should serve it unquestioningly, turn myself inside out for it. Everyone says I ought to write a book or make a movie about my life. For God's sake, I'm twenty years old, though I tell everyone I'm twenty-two.

There's something fake about celebrity. I remember Johnny Mervin posing as an anti-censorship crusader during all the hoopla at Eden. I don't mind being famous in the clubs and having people come to see my show. I'm in control of what I do there, of defining myself. But being a spokeswoman flattens my details, abbreviates me. I become bigger and smaller at the same time, reduced to my basic elements, frozen. I realize how much I like my privacy. It seems so contradictory, given that I take my clothes off for a living.

I am hoping, hoping as I tear open the envelope. I yank back the red cover of *Origins,* scanning the index for my nom de plume, my L. Lee Tracey. I'd wanted an initial at the front of my name, like e.e. cummings or H.D—a held-in part of myself, a modesty, yet something sharp and precise. It's a name to differentiate me from my other selves—not Fonda, not Linda, but L. Lee.

My poem is there, I see it on page sixty-five, my first published poem, nestled in the middle of one whole page.

Sick at early thirty,
feeling apprehensively the suck of
future peel the calm from
smooth and creaseless pearls
of me. Unblemished, soft
and dropping fruit, what ground
will have the thud of me.
I'm stabbed —
my stem does not support
my swollen wholeness
anymore. Untie the knot
that fastens me, unknot
the pretty bow of precepts

wrapped around this flushing brow—
let go.

I am published, I want to scream, I am a poet, the only stripper poet in Canada, maybe in the world—Miss Nude Poet Laureate. I show it to my friends in the bars on rue St. Denis, at launches and parties, jamming it into their faces—proof of my existence, confirmation of my talent. I show it to the girls in the clubs. Sheba shakes her head with the incredulity of someone who's just seen Martians landing.

"This here says you're thirty. You're not thirty," she protests.

"It's way of getting to a feeling," I try to explain. "Turning thirty's a metaphor for change."

"Uh huh. How much they pay you?"

"That's not the point, Sheba."

"How much?"

"Five dollars."

"You gonna buy yourself a doughnut to celebrate?"

Maybe Sheba's being snarly because I'm not seeing her or the other girls so much—I'm keeping my promise to myself to work only part-time, once every two months. My absence makes my friendships in the clubs remoter, and a sliver of suspicion wedges between us. There's always a feeling of betrayal when girls move on or away, a sense that other people are being abandoned. Perhaps I am migrating—I still love the clubs and the adrenaline they pump into me, but

I don't need them as much. I'm finding other sensations among the artists and my own writing. And in television too.

After being interviewed a couple of times on a local talk show, I'm amazed when I'm offered work as a field reporter. I start making guest appearances, talking about offbeat subjects like all-night eateries, gabbing enthusiastically. I learn how to avoid looking directly into the camera and to talk clearly and not slur my words together too quickly. I love doing research—calling up strangers on official business, having the liberty to ask questions. I move through the city with a sense of purpose, carrying my real identity like a secret. But a lot of people have firm ideas of what I am.

There's always a commotion when I arrive in the studio, extra crew members who hover, wanting to get a glimpse of me, I think. The host is a straight old guy, coiffed and made up like a corpse. But he's decent and doesn't make a big deal that I'm a stripper. He likes my reports and encourages me on camera. The woman producer is kind, too, protective, and she shoos away the crew. The two of them make me feel confident of my ability, but after a few months they say there's no more money to keep me on. I thud to the ground, disappointed. I wonder if some fat cat in a top-floor office thinks it's too risqué to have me on TV.

I fit uneasily back into the world, unsure of my talent and the rules of engagement, about my right to occupy other spaces. The further away I go from the clubs, the more I crave their assurances and instant familiarity. Some days I feel so jumpy, swirling in my thoughts, trying to tame my fingers to stay on the typewriter keys. I float into vagueness, imagining the long escape route to my next self. I know I can't be a stripper forever, not even part-time—just the simple force of gravity will eventually pull whatever beauty I have to the floor. But that's not what I'm afraid of. The real terror is choosing what I want to be and becoming it. Everything is so murky outside the clubs; there are so many possibilities, and none. Stripping has always been a current moving me along. Changing that course, making the strip-a-thon, required such vigour, and still the clubs returned to their regular habits—even worse ones. I don't know if change can really happen, inside of me or out, or if life is just inevitable. I'm scared I'll drift into oblivion, uncontained and rootless because I don't exist.

The clubs are swallowing us whole, eating up our genius. The go-gos are becoming the main attraction, pushing the strip shows to the sidelines. They're so different-looking now, skinny like models, with long bony legs and flat chests, unformed and almost boyish. They don't possess the definateness of the older girls, or the femaleness and individual personalities. They prance around, looking away vaguely, or contemplating their own bodies, separated from their experience, suspended. It's the same vacuousness I'm reading about in my John Berger book, *Ways of Seeing*.

There's a connection between how women were depict-
ed in the art of the Middle Ages and now—in clubs
and billboards, a similar emptiness and serenity, the
waiting to be filled by male attention. These go-gos are
the newer, nuder version of the pliant, adoring good
girl. It's as if the audiences or the owners want to
reduce their experience to watching incomplete
women, children. I've tried not to be that all these years
but I can't stop it from happening around me. I can't
even explain it to the girls, who grip their *Cosmo* and
Elle magazines, trying to mimic what they see, believing they are legitimate. Underneath, they're scared and
unsure, flinching on any sharp words or doubts.

The routines are changing too—the go-gos do
their same old quick strips, but they're also being cor-
ralled on stage together, fifteen or twenty of them at a
time, undifferentiated. We call it the meat market and
the go-gos don't like doing it, but they're too unsure to
defy these new rules. We strippers hate it too; our
twenty-minute shows don't have the bang of twenty
naked girls on stage. And the men don't have the same
concentration, the same willingness to wait for the
whole experience. Sometimes I wonder if they think
they're watching television. They want immediate
thrills and sensations—*The Dukes of Hazard* or
Charlie's Angels, noise and skin and a fast-paced zap-
ping on their nerves.

I can't dance as well on the new, brightly lit circu-
lar stages. The clubs are building them so the audience
can look at girls from every angle. But it ruins the illu-

sion, the power of a single girl under a single light, shimmering in the surrounding dark. There's less place to concentrate my attention, no stage front, no delineation of space. Star quality, performance, imagination are dying in the hard light of voyeurism.

I have to work hard to keep myself intact, to push myself through the narrowing expectations of the audience, the noise and distractions. My celebrity helps. People want to see a famous stripper and they think my good deeds makes me less threatening, safer. I can still hook in a less adoring crowd, stop their eyes from wandering to the go-go girls or porn films, get them laughing. They're so desperate to laugh, so grateful to let loose a bellyful. Real laughter's rare now, I don't know when it disappeared, but it has, leaving mean and derisive snorts and snickering. Laughter sounds like hope to me, or forgiveness, and I bask in my own power to conjure it. But then a bunch of suits will arrive, or students, cutting off my connection with their instant need for attention. Sometimes I think they're competing with me for centre stage.

Then the clubs bring in table dancing, and it hardly makes sense to have strippers at all. Sometimes fifteen go-gos are wiggling on their separate boxes during my show—it looks like a Roman orgy out there, men's eyes firmly planted on a thigh, a belly, a breast, only a nose away from them. Often they don't even watch the girls in front of them, but eye each other, cocking their chins in cool superiority or skittish envy, as if they're comparing their cars.

A whole new breed of men moves in, weird, rich guys, computer nerds, stockbroker types who like throwing money around. Sometimes a group of college kids pools their dollars for a few table dances, but they're cut out and ignored by the girls who circle the bigger spenders. The standard price is five dollars a song but some pay ten or twenty; one guy comes in every Thursday and pays sixty dollars for a single dance. Some of them don't even want the girls to dance, they just talk to them. Men are getting strange, fixating on weird little fetishes—pigtails, high heels, bare feet, tattoos, girls who dance to particular songs, who look right at them or who look sullenly away. It's as if the men can only find expression through tiny, specific parts of themselves—sometimes it's anger or arrogance, domination or humiliation. Men are being reduced into smaller bits of themselves, just like the girls. I feel sorry for a lot of the guys. For all of us.

The go-gos are raking it in, some are making five hundred dollars a night in tips and table dances. A lot of strippers have stopped doing shows and become go-go dancers because of the big money. Fewer of us have the strength or the stomach to compete with table dancing. Even Sheba can't withstand it.

"No way I'm selling myself for loose change, girl," she grouses. "There are prostitutes and there are whores, and them girls are whores." I don't think that's true but Sheba grows even more distant, ignoring the girls and creating a cold space around herself. The girls glower back at her.

I've seen it before, the disconnecting; it's part of
moving on. Nobody ever says good-bye, girls sneak
out of the clubs into other lives, suddenly vanishing.
Sheba says she has to go to Chicago to visit her family and she never comes back. She never writes, either.
I lose her abruptly and now I'm alone, a relic at twenty-one, as out of date as Yvette once was.

CHAPTER 10

All Dressed Up and Nowhere to Go

Crazy, bad girls don't need the clubs anymore. They're working in the galleries and alternative spaces, doing performance art. I see them playing with dance and poetry, using sound and movement and burning stares to plough into their renegade selves. I go there too, performing with my friends. One night I bite into a hundred apples to illustrate the original sins of intelligence and fatness. Another time I am laced with elastic strings and try to hurtle free of my puppet master. These are experimental shows, as loopy and precious as what we used to do at Eden with our clothes off.

I hardly exist in the clubs, dancing only once every two months, annoyed at the intrusion of having to make my thousand dollars and at the erosion of what I loved most about the clubs. But I still need to perform, to exercise my wilder impulses and to break their laws. I like to throw my body into the air of those places, feeling my sweat and pulsing self, living in the unpredictable spray of the men's needs and attentions and in the danger of rejection. I return for my annual Tits for Tots, enjoying the producing and designing of the show, and the chance to redeem myself and the girls. But it's never as true as the first year, never as hopeful. There's less chance of changing the course of things; hardly anyone remembers what stripping used to be, what we used to be when we had faces.

It is in the blur of planning the third Christmas show that a producer and director from the National Film Board ask to film my gala. They call themselves women, not girls. They're from Studio D, they tell me, a women's studio. My second skin slips on, the armoured one. The two women back into their feminism cautiously when I first meet them, telling me that all women are sisters, meaning me and them, I guess. They want to understand stripping and to film the girls in my gala. They say they're making a documentary, which I figure means one of those nature, newsy programs—all shaky and boring and narrated. It's supposed to be an educational film on female sexuality and pornography. I guess I'm the sexuality part. I talk with the girls about letting the women film and they get excited thinking Hollywood's calling. I warn them that it's something dull and educational, and maybe a chance to explain ourselves, but they cling to their hope. Until they see the two women up close.

The filmmakers look funny in the club, like everybody's mother. They seem middle-aged and floppy in their baggy clothes. The girls curl away from them, wondering why I let them in. There's an unspoken code in the clubs, one I carry around in my own head—if you don't look like a girl, you can't think like one either. We judge each other by our beauty and clothes as much as men do. I'm the only one getting away with not shaving my legs or not wearing makeup because of who I am, but girls who hide their femininity are immediately suspect.

I tell the girls not to worry, that the National Film Board will do a classy job showing us for who we are. I don't know that for sure, but they're the NFB, makers of films I saw all through my childhood, about poor people and Indians and Newfoundland fishermen. Anyway, I'm starting to like the younger-looking one, the director—she seems more open and just a little awkward. Late in the night she films herself putting on makeup in front of the dressing-room mirror, pretending to be a stripper, I think. I have to chuckle—yeah, sure, we're all sisters. The girl's got her Madonna routine down pat against my Mary Magdalene.

A few weeks later the two women ask me to join them as a partner on their film journey—they want to go all over the United States looking at strip clubs and peep shows and live sex acts, things we don't have in Canada. I'm wonderful and articulate, they say. They're even more amazed that I've read so much feminist literature. I like surprising them, but I don't forget they're the feminist enemy, casting shadows on the clubs and on our right to exist. But I want to know them now, to compare their ideas with mine. I want to see what lies at the edges of striptease, to stop flinching from the porn films and table dancing. I need to understand their wider meaning, to connect the dots and see what patterns emerge.

The girls in the clubs don't want to notice the changes or discuss them. Sometimes I feel so lonely, wishing I had Emma or Yvette to talk to, someone with a memory of how things used to be. The girls now just want to rush into their money, they just shrug at the humiliations, keeping their hurt and sourness for the dressing room and each other. *"C'est le business,"* they sigh, not daring to feel more.

Doing the film seems like an instant education. I'm not sure what pornography is. Am I supposed to be pornography? I don't think so. I don't like competing with the porno films in the clubs or seeing the tits and asses all over the billboards and magazine covers. It's those magazines the girls compare themselves to, that put ideas in their heads. They're as bad as the hard-core stuff, I think, sneaky and acceptable. I want to do the film. I feel a thrill push through my mind— maybe it's the sense of danger. It will take months to film, I'm told, months of coming and going and of juggling my schedule. The women offer me three thousand dollars, the equivalent of three weeks of stripping. It doesn't seem like much. I wonder how big their salaries are.

I'm not quite sure what I'm supposed to be doing in the film, besides going along and watching things. I'm no expert on porn, so I guess my job is to bring another, looser point of view. I don't know anything about making films either, but I know how small the news people can make me. I tell the women I want all my parts included, the poetry, the home, the performance art. I want to be whole so people know that strippers are complicated and not just bodies. That's my condition, and they agree.

The director and I are both astonished we like each other. She says I'm more comfortable in my body than she is, as if she's envious. She's more open-minded than I thought, less condescending, but I'm still cautious—with all her education and film credentials she must think I'm alien and small. I wonder if she's just a middle-class tourist, using me as her ticket into an exposé. Maybe she wants to catch me, to make me admit that what I do is dirty. It isn't, but the shows that are going on around me are harder to explain. I don't want her disliking those girls, though, judging them harshly. They're my friends.

The filming begins at my studio, with me at my typewriter. Trucksful of equipment are hauled into my tiny place, lights and cameras that make me seem important. I'm more equal with my clothes on, talking

about my poetry and striptease. I'm surer of the director now that she knows this part of me. I trust her for
the journey into America.

New York is a shock—42nd Street is the tackiest
place I've ever seen. There aren't stages and shows like
the clubs back home, they're more like sex emporiums.
I'm not sure the director knows the difference or if she
lumps all public nudity together. One whole building
is divided by floors into specialties, like a department
store—there are movies on the first floor, peep shows
on the second, live shows on the third. The place
reminds me of a horror house—dark, winding corri-
dors and sectioned-off cubicles along the sides. There's
a sharp sting of Lysol everywhere. The girls sit or
dance in glass-covered cages, like zoo animals. Some of
them do live sex shows with each other; others sit
behind steel walls that roll up at the sound of a quar-
ter and talk dirty through a telephone. I don't get it,
it's just so fake and ugly. These girls aren't strippers or
go-go girls. They're in another league. I like them,
though, I can feel their twitchiness, how scared they
are of being looked down on. Every one of them hurries to tell us how they're working through college, or
supporting their kids, or have appeared on some TV
show. I know their ache so deeply, their urge to be
decent. We should film them at home, I think, we
should get to the other layers of their humanness, but
the crew says we can't, for reasons they don't explain.

The crew is uncomfortable, unsure how to react
to these gaping wounds. The girls are afraid of me,

too, thinking I'm straight and powerful, and that my opinion counts. I tell them I'm a stripper and they relax. We fall into an abbreviated talk about money and management, but their slang is different and their hurt is harder. We're not completely the same and I'm relieved. But the director says they remind her of the go-go girls back home at the meat market. I see it too and it bugs me.

The director is more assured among the feminists and porn critics and I'm the shaky one. We meet Robin Morgan of *Ms.* magazine and the editor of *Sisterhood Is Powerful,* Emma's favourite book. Wouldn't she choke to see me here. We film Robin at home, we'll film all the feminists that way, in their own worlds, surrounded by their trinkets, not swallowed up in ugly places like the porn girls. Robin reclines on her sofa with her husband and son. She's charming and welcoming and I can tell her mind is lively and elastic; she's not one of those knuckle-faced man-haters. She talks about the poison of pornography, how it seeps into our relationships and makes real women cutouts. She worries about her son learning about women through pornography, how it will damage his masculinity and his own open heart.

Does striptease do that, I wonder, do I do that? No, I give them something more, I'm inside myself on stage, I don't need to feel guilty. But there are the porn films playing through my show, distracting the men. They're learning about me from that, comparing me to the lie up there. I hate that part.

For hours Robin weaves the strands of her arguments, making us laugh and cry. It must be her beauty and nice clothes that help open me, because what she says is not a lot different from Kate Millet, the lesbian artist and writer, but I cringe from Kate. She is enormous in her bulky wool sweater, with her long, stringy hair. She's not chatty or warm, just matter-of-fact about the certain evil of pornography. The director and crew are completely reverential. Kate is on the floor of her studio working on one of her paintings. I sit farther back, away from her, watching, listening. She talks about women being queens and goddesses in history, about men's violent overthrow of our power, the market economy as an assertion of that dominance and of women being traded and sold. It's all such stiff and hardened talk, yet her voice winds around the words, soft and sure. I watch her fingers move delicately, the sensuous lines of her drawings. There's such beauty in her fingertips, in what she's doing, such a contrast to her sloppy exterior. Maybe she's living inside herself, in ideas and art, with soft tongue and breath. She possesses a strange sort of sensuality, as fierce and true as Ruby's, and as assured. She lives beyond her external shell and I managed to find her; I stumble past the ugly cliché of the fat and furious feminist. All these years I've been wincing at people's stereotypes of me, and here I am doing the same thing. I like this new mental agility, it's Kate's gift to me. But I still don't buy all of her male-conspiracy theories.

There are a lot of stupid things we do in the film: buying chocolate penises and boobs, trying on sexy lingerie. I think it's a diversion from the more serious stuff. Filming requires such alertness, talking to strangers, incorporating what they know, stringing all the parts of pornography together. I am exhausted and acutely alive at the same time. But I keep waiting for the lightening bolt, for the moment when I'll be accused of being pornographic. But I see the connection only dimly, in the continuum between soft and hard core, maybe in the meat market stuff.

There's a seriousness to porn, a lack of humour and playfulness in the films, the sex shows, magazines, but I know how much the men in the clubs long to laugh, how bored and numb they get just gawking. I don't think there's anything wrong with nude strip acts or even those live sex shows, if they're attached to a whole personality. Hard core's different—the rapes and animals, the viciousness and humiliation can feed a twisted mind, but that has nothing to do with me. And even some of that is harmless. The whole crew is flinching at all the bondage stuff, but I think a lot of it's a send-up or a consensual thing. We're so busy looking at all the visual cues, but is the Queen an S&M freak because she wears riding boots? Pornography's stealing a lot of fun images but it doesn't make those images pornographic. Does it?

Wisconsin takes my breath away. We're interviewing a sociologist who's done lab tests on porn and violence.

He shows different kinds of porn films to male students—soft core, hard, and then he asks the guys to
administer shocks to women who, they're told, are taking tests. When a woman gives a wrong answer the boys
are supposed to give her a shock, and they can control
the duration and voltage. The more violent the porn
they've just seen, the harder and longer they punish
wrong answers. The shocks aren't real, but the guys
don't know that.

We don't see a session, but just hearing about it
makes my skin cold. The sociologist says that when
men see porn they grow numb to women's real pain,
and that the film gives them the permission to inflict
it. Even the nonviolent porn, the kind they're playing
back home in the clubs, has an effect, he says. I feel
horrified and angry and I don't want to believe it, but
I can't escape it either. This is hard, cold fact, scientif-
ic proof, not politics or middle-class prissiness about
sex. If pornography affects behaviour in the men who
watch it, does it have an effect on the women who do
it, on those girls in the booths in New York, or in magazines? What about strippers?

For all our nosing around, the producer and director still haven't got to the top floor of pornography:
the porno queens and filmmakers, the major girlie
magazines. I don't know why we can't get at them, why
we're spending so much time with the live sex girls.
For all their sad and ugly sex shows, they're marginal,
they don't occupy the same space in the public imagination or reach the biggest audience. The clubs, and

maybe the sex shows, are still social events, regulated by internal and external rules. What's needed is improved wages and working conditions for the girls. Better live shows could be an antidote to the numbing of pornography. It's getting them good that's the problem. I think the magazines and films are where the big bucks are and where the violence is. Finally, we all fly out to Los Angeles, trying to get inside *Playboy* or *Hustler* magazine. What we end up with is a woman photographer who does picture layouts for *Hustler*. I'm eager to see her. I want to know how she manufactures those images and what being in them does to the women.

Suze is British, I think, chatty and kinetic. She loves shooting porn but she says it in a big, showy way, as if she's convincing herself. I like her because she needs to be liked. She's afraid of us, I think. Today Suze is shooting an S&M spread she calls "Pirate and His Moll Rape an Innocent Victim." There's an amazing shiplike set with costumes and props and a long sword to threaten the victim with. It's all so stupid, almost laughable.

The two female models are jittery as they get made up in the back. I watch them disappear behind the makeup and costumes, getting louder and more vulgar as they move into their roles. The makeup girl colours their nipples and covers the pimples on their bums. There's even so-called pussy juice to make their labias glisten. The male model swaggers in, demanding everyone's attention—he's laughable too. The three of them arrive on set in their get-ups and start winding around each other in clumsily suggestive poses. Suze directs them to take this off, that, to expose more boobs, to look afraid, to spread their legs, to get the knife closer to the throat. Again and again they move around each other, acting and stripping and faking sex. After a while, the giggling gives way to tedium.

I want to pose, too, not in a group but by myself. I want to get to the feeling of it, to the seam between fake and real. I need to know if the creation of this image is all external or if it gets inside. Suze loves the idea and takes me to the dressing room where I put on a corset. Then I get made up, thickly, in a way I'd never dream of as a stripper. I tell Suze that I just want to model for the camera and take a few directions.

Suze props me on a bed with the sword and arranges my body parts into poses. She starts directing me in a low, soft voice. I let myself float. It's so easy to make my lips pout, to thrust out my chest and chin, to lower my eyes in that girlie-mag pose. I know these positions almost intuitively, they're all here inside me, probably inside every woman. Suze keeps coaxing and I respond, moving an arm, tilting my chin. She tells me to lift my knee, to rest my head there, *to open up, open up, open up.* I can resist, I won't spread my legs, *open up, open up,* I probably look uptight, what am I afraid of anyway, *open up, open up,* I want to get to the feeling don't I? I want to understand this objectification, *open up, open up.* What the hell, just this once, I spread my legs.

"Pussy juice, get me the pussy juice," Suze hollers. The makeup girl scurries toward me and dabs my labia with baby oil. I'm making stupid grimaces, trying to laugh off my embarrassment—what the hell am I doing? I get a flash of Ruby that first night in Eden, spreading her legs so easily in the dressing room, so completely attached. This is nothing like that.

Everyone's holding her breath, I'm holding mine, as Suze's camera clicks in the silence and the film camera watches. I feel myself disappearing, reduced to my physical components, fading into the tightness of panic, pulling myself up, getting hold of my borders. That's it, I can't do it anymore. I pull my knee down and hunch over, letting my legs dangle limply from the bed.

No one knows what to say. The director comes over and puts her arm around me. I feel sick, disemboweled. What was I thinking? All right, okay, I know the sensation now, it feels like Sean in Newfoundland, it feels like rape. I'm swelling up with rage, I want to make Suze see what she's done but I don't want to hurt her. She's so damned vulnerable.

Suze says I did great and she wants me to agree. I tell her I feel humiliated and violated. It wasn't fun at all. One of the models hears me and starts crying and Suze bolts from the set. The model says she felt awful too but that she can't tell Suze because it's her first porn job and she needs the money. I follow Suze into the bathroom and find her heaving in great, shaking sobs. She tells me no one's ever complained before, that they've always said they were having fun. I feel so sorry for her. Who am I to judge how another woman makes her money? All I can do is say how it affects me.

It is a wet and sloppy afternoon and I am stinging. After the shoot, I don't want to see the crew or to talk. I order room service and ball up alone in my room. The next day they film me on an empty beach describing the feelings I had in front of Suze's camera. It seems so beside the point, this is not a film about me, but I go along. Maybe people need to know how porn feels. I did. My mind is still gummed up with hurt; I need to get out of it. I walk down the beach, far away from the others, and dance alone in my bathing suit, stretching my limbs, slapping my long hair against my face and back, letting the wind touch me, the wet sand. I need the freedom of movement and beauty, the clear wisdom of my own body. I spin again and again, swooping down into a squat so my thigh muscles ache with my weight. I love myself again in this movement, I feel my strength and ability, a pureness that sweeps my mind clean. A man in the distance approaches slowly, watching me. I don't mind, the dance is a gift. He hovers for many minutes, then pulls out a camera. I ask him not to shoot me, to leave me alone, but he says he's with a newspaper. I feel hunted suddenly, split apart. He says he's got the right to shoot me, it's a public beach. I try chasing him away, arguing with him, but he digs into the sand defiantly. My world tilts. He doesn't want to enjoy my dance, I realize, he wants to reduce it to an image and to possess that image. I'm not even real to him, or the source of the magic, I'm an impediment. It's so opposite to the power I feel on stage, to the spontaneous and whole body experience of performing, to the way I want to live. I go still and stop dancing to protect myself. I finally walk away defeated.

The filmmakers and I shoot sporadically over the next few months and then the crew vanishes and the director leaves the country for a year. All the bits of our journey hang in a cutting room at the NFB, where an editor strings them together.

Months go by and then the women from the National Film Board show me the film. I'm stunned. They huddle around me, wanting me to like it, needing me to. I have to stop myself from shaking. How do you tell someone you like that you feel betrayed and sickened?

I can't believe I'm the star of the film, the one holding it together. I can't believe what they've turned me into. There's nothing of my studio or my performance art, nothing of me outside my function. I'm reduced to a porno queen, me, the softest thing in the film, the stripper who doesn't spread, immortalized as a cheap cliché and the "articulate" voice of all the live sex girls. Why couldn't the filmmakers find a well-spoken porn queen? And the Suze shoot, it's all there in long, lingering colour—God, there's even a zoom-in. I'd never have done it if I'd known it would be used that way. And the scene on the beach—it looks like I'm bleeding from being a stripper instead of reeling from that day with Suze. Then at the end I'm a snappy, happy, born-again feminist penitent—a bad girl gone good. The film takes credit for my supposed conversion, as if I had no intellectual context before.

The women tell me they couldn't fit my other details in the film. They say that people love me, that all the test screenings are full of admiration for me. How can people feel that when they don't even know me, when what I am has been erased? What they're admiring is an invention. I try telling the women what I feel, they can see it in my face, but I'm not forceful enough, I don't want to hurt them. I don't even know if I should trust my instincts. Maybe I'm being too self-protective. The women tell me that people have a hard time seeing themselves in a film. All I can be grateful for is that it's an educational film and hardly anyone will see it.

For weeks the filmmakers chase after me, calling me at home, wanting me to like the film, explaining how important it is, and the issue. I feel pressured into presenting a common front, into his show of Madonna and Whore Do Pornoland Together. I still like the director, but I don't think she understands the hurt in me, the humiliation.

There's a buzz building around the film, a humming in my network of friends. It worries me. The "educational" film gets a prestigious screening at the Toronto Film Festival, and another is scheduled at a benefit for *Ms.* magazine in New York. I wake up one morning to a huge photograph of me from the Suze shoot in *The Globe and Mail*. It crushes me—I feel exploited, the same way the filmmakers say pornography exploits other women.

Later, in New York, the women ask me to pose with Linda Lovelace, another feminist darling who's written a book about her days as Deep Throat. There's no connection between her and me except in the minds of the press and my new feminist sisters. I'm stinging with rage, divided in myself about what to do. I feel a loyalty to these filmmakers, I've learned things by doing their film, my own thinking has accelerated, my understanding of what pornography is and how it poisons. These women have given me confidence to trust my feelings about pornography, that *I'm* not alone in disliking some of it. But I'm not pornography. I think snuff films are abhorrent, and kiddie porn, and the mean stuff. I want to talk about what I've seen, how even the clubs I know are changing, but I want to protect the history of striptease, what it was and could be. I want people to distinguish between the shades and grades, to know the subtleties and where the real menace lies. There's a huge ideological difference between me and the filmmakers, and maybe some feminists who think all public nudity is an assault on female dignity. I know the difference, I've lived it. What I do is very unlike what the girls in New York do. But I can't make the point clearly enough. It seems everyone in North America wants the fairy tale about the bad girl turning good. I'm suddenly a girl with a past, but it's not my past.

I wish I could just go underground, hide from the hoopla, but I can't—the film is too enormous. It's all over the magazines and talk shows, on radio and television throughout North America. My life is being portrayed, my motives and morals debated, everywhere. I try to inject my own thinking and opinions, my real experience, but I often feel like someone's pet being paraded at screenings and women's talks, or that my opinions are being expropriated by more vigorous arguments. There are epiphanies: often I'm moved by other women's testimonials, how they open up to me and describe their wounds and experiences, the pain of being female. The film has an enormous power, it's a catalyst, allowing all kinds of secrets to spill out. I find that valuable, sacred, and I am awed by the privilege of sharing it. Thousands of women all over the continent claim me as their personal heroine, some of them corner me in laundromats and restaurants and dentist's offices, whispering reverentially. The adoration is soothing and terrible. I'm not their Madonna; it's not my pain or courage they see on screen and are empowered by. My real courage is in withstanding all this fiction and trying to claim my own ideas, my own self in this media storm. I have to reassure myself often that I am the owner of my thoughts—I have to reach into my mind, feel for the patterns of ideas, proving the evolution of my own thinking to myself. The filmmakers didn't invent me, didn't plant ideas in me that weren't already there. I'd been exploring these issues, insisting on my own dignity long before the National Film Board rescued me. Now I am smothering under the weight of the film's lie: that I was re-created and liberated by the filmmakers. It's so humiliating and so subtle a robbery that my mind can barely express it, but my body does. I bite my nails, my hands twitch and my thighs tighten during interviews and talks. This film has done what pornography does: abbreviating my details, overemphasizing certain attributes, caging my essence in a flat, single dimension. It's the same theft I felt with the photographer on the California beach—the killing of spontaneity and instinct. It doesn't matter whether it was premeditated or accidental.

I've seen good intentions lead to betrayal before, I know life's lessons often begin with a loss of faith. The film's done now, I'll have to learn to live in the shadow of myself on screen, to compete with that invented self.

Making the film should be a natural end, the one the filmmakers want, but the clubs keep drawing me back: the money, the habit, the adrenaline fortifying me from all my prickly doubts. Stripping is about more than sex, it's illusion, possibility, reinvention. Refuge. Even as it narrows it seems more definite than the real world. The straight world wants to contain us strippers in its own image, reducing us to sexual caricatures. The feminists don't seem able to separate us from the porno queens, and pornography lies about all of us. I'm confused about so many things, including my own complicity.

I want to make the clubs better. Even after the film, I try to barricade us strippers from the fall that is coming, from all that American pollution. I immerse myself in the clubs, to talk myself into believing again, but I see too many reminders of the girls in New York—the commodifying, the money, the small stages and diminishing spaces. I am angry at the other strippers and go-gos for not trying harder, for hoarding all their hope and energy for our Christmas gala—like Christians who only go to church at Easter. Believing in ourselves is a full-time job, requiring vigilance and force. I can't hold up the standards with just a few others, I don't know why I think I have to. It's time for me to leave, I've lived my experience, earned my wisdom. I've arrived through my own door and I can't grow old here. I worry about what I'll become, about money and where to make it. I've saved some, but not enough for a clean and easy escape.

It happens on a Thursday, during my second show at J.C.'s smaller club. The place is almost empty and the porn film is humming behind the stage. I watch the men watching the screen, then looking slack-jawed at me. "See ya later," I say, leaving the stage half-dressed. "Dat's it and dat's all," I chuckle to myself.

I twitch for weeks, wondering about a ritual to mark my final parting, something definite to separate my selves. I decide on Mont Royal, the place I most adore, and go there just after dawn, alone. I bring my Dietrich costume and one of Yvette's silk dresses and a pair of scissors. Up on the knoll behind Beaver Lake I cut the fabric to shreds, flinching behind my tears with so many emotions. I try to remember clearly Eden and Emma, Chicago and Merrill, to visualize the toothless men in the frozen northern villages, Sheba, Ruby, the Miss Nude Canada Pageant, Tits for Tots, my first show, Ric, but the memories are vague, tangled under the harsher outlines of that creep Valle, Chesty Morgan, Sean in Newfoundland, the stick girls who crowd on stage.

It is grief I feel. So much has disappeared from the clubs. Who will remember us? We were amazing once, gutsy and strong. We'd resisted, refusing to be what we were told to be. We'd created our own space and our own selves. We'd been generous to each other, and forgiving. It is a culture and a history I'm leaving, as precious to me as anything can be. Now it's a dark and embarrassing mark on other people's history, something to be erased. And ashamed of.

I sit on the picnic table and try to imagine the great big vastness that stretches out ahead of me.

Afterword

It was always tricky explaining that I'd been a stripper once; it was startling to other sensibilities, as harsh a class distinction as one can make. People reacted with suspicion, pity or sometimes prurient fascination. They leaped into their assumptions, imagining me a whore, an idiot, a victim. I winced, not from my shame, because there really wasn't any, but from the shame people wanted to impose. I moved into radio, television, acting and filmmaking always the ex-stripper, diminished somehow, suspect.

I loved striptease, its snubbing of authority, its vague promises that hung in the air. There was such raw humanness in those clubs, a condensing of life's contradictions and a razor sharp intersection of corporate and individual interests. I learned to see into the secrets of the heart, to measure human worth. I became a writer there. Striptease was a way into self, a set of circumstances to grow in. I was so young then, so tender, that remembering has brought a twinge of melancholy, a realization that the internal self hardens and conforms to smaller realities.

The time I lived as a stripper was different, more tolerant of excess and personal drama, safer to experiment in. There was less need for consistency and conformity, more chances to express all of my impulses. I believed, still believe, that strip clubs were gateways to more authentic ways of being. Certainly the mid-seventies was the last good time to be a stripper, just before television had completely swallowed our imagination, before the corporate agenda made us homogeneous and hard-core pornography spread its numbing venom. After that, striptease became business-driven and mechanical and the genius of strippers disappeared under the tyranny of explicitness. Striptease fell from grace because the world stopped dreaming. Literalness killed the wonder of illusion and the eye replaced the heart in the act of seeing. I grieve the loss of striptease and for what has replaced it, I grieve for the disappearance of my own younger, surer self who could stand naked on a strip-club stage and see into the humanity of strangers.